EVERYMAN'S LIBRARY

100

FICTION

Everyman, I will go with thee, and be thy guide,
In thy most need to go by thy side

FERNANDO DE ROJAS

CELESTINA

OR
THE TRAGI-COMEDY OF
CALISTO AND MELIBEA

TRANSLATED BY
PHYLLIS HARTNOLL, M.A., L.-ès-L.

LONDON   J. M. DENT & SONS LTD
NEW YORK   E. P. DUTTON & CO INC

INTRODUCTION

THE *Tragicomedia de Calisto y Melibea*, or, as it is usually called, *La Celestina*, stands second only to *Don Quixote* in the history of Spanish literature, and is hardly less important in the history of European literature in general. Its influence was particularly marked on the novel and on the drama, in both of which categories it might claim to be included. Its length and style seem to indicate that it was intended for a reading public; but it is written throughout in dialogue so vivid that, although it lacks all stage directions and indications of change of scene, one can nevertheless envisage it as a play. There is no record of its having been acted in its original form, or at the time of its first appearance, but it has been adapted for the stage many times, and in recent years has proved successful in modern versions both in Spain and in France.

The origins and authorship of *Celestina* are alike obscure, though its history since publication is well documented, and it has been the subject of much scholarly controversy. The first extant edition—of which only one copy has survived, and that lacking the title-page—was printed at Burgos in 1499. There may have been an earlier edition. A further edition was printed at Seville in 1501. Both these editions contained only sixteen acts, as against the final total of twenty-one, which were printed in the three separate editions of 1502. That the book quickly became popular is attested by the numerous reprints—many with woodcut illustrations—of the sixteenth century. Interest in it slackened in the seventeenth century, which has so far yielded only eight editions up to 1632. From then until 1835 no further editions were called for, but the latter part of the nineteenth century saw a revival of interest, particularly among scholars, who busied themselves collating the early editions and providing introductions and notes to the reprints. In 1909 a facsimile edition of the unique 1499 copy was published in a limited edition of 400 copies by Archer M. Huntington. A standard text, based on the first complete (1502) editions, is now readily available in inexpensive editions.

If the date of composition and first publication of *Celestina* is still in doubt, so is the question of its authorship. It is commonly attributed to Fernando de Rojas, whose name is revealed in acrostic form in a set of verses prefixed to the second edition. In a letter accompanying the verses he says he has done nothing but continue and prepare for publication an unfinished manuscript which came into his hands by chance. It consisted of the long first act only, and may have been written, he says, by one of two earlier poets, Juan de Mena or Rodrigo Cota. This may be so, or it may be merely a polite fiction, a transparently modest disclaimer of authorship of a type familiar to all students of literature. All we can be sure of is that someone was responsible for the one long and fifteen shorter acts that make up the first draft of the book, and that someone—de Rojas or another (and scholars have put forward several claimants)—added in the edition of 1502 five further acts, made up of that part of the story which lies between Lucretia's reply to Melibea in Act XIV, 'No, madam, I slept all the time' (p. 161), and her exclamation in Act XIX: 'Listen, listen! Something terrible has happened!' (p. 197). So there may have been one author, or two, or even three. In the absence of documentary proof, their identification must rest on internal evidence. Enough for our present purpose that the book was written, and that here we have it, complete in its twenty-one acts.

It is interesting to note that once the book became well known the original title, which gives pride of place to the young lovers, was replaced by the name of the old woman whose machinations set the plot in motion and bring about the final tragedy. It was in an edition of 1559, printed in Alcalá, that Calisto and Melibea first gave way to Celestina, the old bawd who dominates the action even after her death, and who is so vividly depicted, both in her own conversations and in the descriptions given of her by the other characters, that she dwarfs everyone else. She is evil incarnate, always about the devil's business; but there is such splendour in her ruthlessness, so much vigour and directness in her realistic outlook, that she is unforgettable. Her precepts and practice make a mockery of all those *chevaleresque* ideals against which Cervantes was to do battle more than a century later. The orchard in which Calisto and Melibea meet is a fit place for young love, perhaps, but it is near neighbour of Celestina's sordid hovel; Calisto's enjoyment of Melibea is essentially no different from that of his servant's of the prostitute Areusa; the ignoble deaths of Parmeno and Sempronio are paralleled by that of Calisto, who slips from a ladder and dashes out his brains as he rushes to confront a non-existent danger. Each action of the story, as it unfolds, is a wry commentary on the noble romanticism of the popular legendary heroes.

Yet somehow romance comes creeping back. There is a poetic beauty in the story of the young couple, who join the long procession of 'star-crossed lovers'; there is a diabolic beauty in the towering figure of Celestina, drunk with a Renaissance flood of words, dabbling in black magic, conjuring the devil, swaying to her purposes the pliant wills of young girls and the lascivious appetites of grown men. Even in her villainy she is single-minded, and never seeks to excuse herself, taking pride in the successful accomplishment of her *métier*.

If Celestina is a vivid personality, who seems to have existed for ever in her own right, she is none the less surrounded by a motley crowd no less vigorous and characteristic. Though the actors in this tragi-comedy are few in number, they bring to life in their conversations a whole world of pushing, jostling citizens, thronging the narrow streets of the bustling city—a city variously

identified as Toledo, Salamanca, or Madrid. It is never named
in the book. Perhaps it never existed in reality; but it stands
four-square in the world of the imagination.

Popular in her own country, Celestina was not long in making
her way into foreign climes. The first French translations of
the book appeared in 1527. German and Italian versions soon
followed. The first known English translation dates from 1631,
and was the work of James Mabbe. The title-page reads *The
Spanish Bawd, represented in Celestina or The Tragicke-Comedy
of Calisto and Melibea, wherein is contained, besides the pleasant-
nesse and sweetenesse of the stile, many philosophicall Sentences
and profitable Instructions necessary for the younger sort; Shewing
the deceits and subtilties housed in the bosomes of false servants
and cunny-catching Bawds.* The translation is, like the original,
racy and bursting with vitality, though in the style of the time
Mabbe tends to decorate the somewhat spare and realistic
dialogue with the conceits and antitheses dear to his contemporaries. He often uses four words where one would do, and
in many places he explains the Spanish in a series of phrases,
each of which throws light on the meaning, the whole adding up
to something more than a mere rendering into English.

It is probable that Mabbe made use of some contemporary
French, or even Italian, versions as well as the original Spanish,
for they were readily available. It is not impossible that he may
also have had something in English to help to lighten his labours,
for in about 1530 Rastell had published—perhaps in his own
adaptation—an interlude entitled *Calisto and Melibea*, based on
the first part of *Celestina*, and probably performed privately.
In 1580 there is a reference to a new stage adaptation, and in
1598 *The Tragicke Comedye of Celestina* was licensed for publication. Both these are now lost, or the projects came to nothing.
They tell us, however, that *Celestina* was current in Shakespeare's
time, and it is tempting to suppose that he knew, or knew of, the
chief characters, though it would be pressing one's conjectures

too far to presume that he consciously used his knowledge. There is no need for Romeo and Juliet to owe anything to Calisto and Melibea, but Juliet's Nurse is surely of the company of Celestina, who would have approved of her advice: 'I think it best you marry with the Countie'?

Mabbe's translation was reprinted in the Tudor Translations in 1893, and again in Routledge's Library of Early Novelists, with an introduction and notes by H. Warner Allen; bound with this latter is *The Interlude of Calisto and Melibea*. Allen thinks that the similarities between Mabbe and the Interlude, where they both differ from the original, indicate that there was a shortened prose version of the story in circulation, founded on the Interlude and used by Mabbe. But might it not equally well be that there was an earlier, lost, English version used by both? Apart from an adaptation in narrative form, interspersed with fragments of the original dialogue, made by Captain John Stevens in 1707, there has been no other version of *Celestina* in English. In 1955 an American version of the original sixteen chapters only was made by Lesley Byrd Simpson, who seems somewhat out of sympathy with his subject, referring to Calisto as 'a sex-ridden egoist' and Melibea as 'a conventional gullible innocent.' Nor does he seem to comprehend the temper of the time, which prevented Calisto and Melibea from solving their problems by a straightforward offer of marriage.

The present translation claims to be no more than a faithful rendering of the original, with such slight adaptations as may help to make it acceptable to a modern reader. Nothing has been added, nothing taken away. Such liberties as have been taken with the text have been confined mostly to the many popular sayings and old proverbs with which it is plentifully enriched. Sometimes the English equivalent came readily to mind; sometimes it had to be searched for; occasionally, where literal translation would have made nonsense, a phrase, different in content, but the same in intention, has been pressed into service.

The parentheses, which in the Spanish editions indicated asides, have been retained in all their inconsistency; and recourse has been had for the solving of knotty problems to the many editions of *Celestina* at the British Museum.

In conclusion, it is to be hoped that those who first make Celestina's acquaintance in this new version will enjoy her company as much as the translator has done.

PHYLLIS HARTNOLL.

London,
   1958.

CONTENTS

The following people take part in this tragi-comedy:

CALISTO, a young lover
MELIBEA, the daughter of Pleberio
PLEBERIO, the father of Melibea
ALISA, the mother of Melibea
CELESTINA, an old bawd
PARMENO
SEMPRONIO
TRISTAN } servants of Calisto
SOSIA
CRITO, a lewd man
LUCRETIA, a maidservant to Pleberio
ELICIA
AREUSA } young prostitutes
CENTURIO, a ruffian

A synopsis of the whole work

CALISTO, a young man of noble birth, intelligent, handsome, well educated, endowed with many good qualities, but of moderate fortune, falls in love with Melibea, a beautiful, high-spirited young woman of spotless reputation and good family, wealthy, the only child and heiress of her father Pleberio, tenderly cherished by her mother Alisa. Calisto, spurred on by his passion, and aided by Celestina, a crafty and wicked old woman, with the help of two of his servants whom she has suborned by promise of pleasure and profit, overcomes Melibea's chaste resistance. The lovers and those who have worked for them come to a disastrous and tragic end. The story begins with an unlucky chance which brings Calisto face to face with Melibea whom he loves.

ACT ONE

SUMMARY: *Calisto, going into an orchard in search of his falcon, there meets Melibea, with whom he is in love; but when he declares his passion, she rebukes him sharply. He returns home in despair, and confides in one of his servants, Sempronio, who with some difficulty persuades him to enlist the help of Celestina, an old bawd in whose house lives Elicia, Sempronio's mistress. When Sempronio calls at Celestina's house on his master's business, Elicia is entertaining another of her lovers, one Crito, whom she hides. While Sempronio is with Celestina Calisto unburdens himself to Parmeno, another of his men. Their conversation is interrupted by the arrival of Sempronio and Celestina. The latter recognizes Parmeno, talks to him of his childhood, and persuades him to make friends with Sempronio.*

CALISTO. In this, Melibea, I recognize the greatness of God.

MELIBEA. In what, Calisto?

CALISTO. In that He has permitted nature to endow you with such beauty, and has allowed me, all unworthy, to meet you alone in so favourable a place, where I can at last disclose to you the torments of my passion. Such bounty, the answer to many prayers and supplications, is far beyond my deserts! When was any man as happy as I at this moment? The saints in glory, who see God face to face, cannot rejoice more than I at the sight of you! But alas, how different are our destinies! They worship without fear, while I, unhappy, dare not remember in what torments I shall be plunged by your absence.

1

MELIBEA. Am I then so precious in your sight?

CALISTO. So precious, believe me, that if God offered me in exchange a seat among His saints in heaven, I would not accept it.

MELIBEA. I will answer you as you deserve, if you speak to me in this manner.

CALISTO. Blessed be my ears, that hear such sweet discourse!

MELIBEA. Curse them, rather, for hearing what I have to say. Your punishment shall be as heavy as your audacity warrants. All your acts and words seek only to dishonour me. Go, wretched man, for I can no longer bear the sight of one who thinks to tempt me with illicit love!

CALISTO. I go, like one overcome by the cruelty of malicious fate. . . . Sempronio, Sempronio? Where are you, you rascal?

SEMPRONIO. I am here, sir, busy about your horses.

CALISTO. My horses? Then what are you doing in that room?

SEMPRONIO. Your falcon flew home. I have put him back on his perch.

CALISTO. The devil take you! May you perish miserably, and suffer torments as keen as those from which death, I hope, will shortly deliver me. Go, wretch, prepare my room, make up my bed!

SEMPRONIO. Sir, it is all ready for you.

CALISTO. Close the shutters! Let darkness encompass my woe, solitude be the companion of my despair. My misery flies from the light of day. O death, how welcome art thou to wretches that summon thee in anguish! Oh, even if those learned doctors Hippocrates and Galen were here now, they could not abate the pain I feel! O Seleucian pity, soften the heart of Pleberio's daughter, and abandon me not to the fate of Pyramus and most unhappy Thisbe!

SEMPRONIO. What is the meaning of this?

CALISTO. Away, you fool, and trouble me no more! Leave me, before my hand strikes you suddenly dead!

SEMPRONIO. I am gone, sir! I leave you to your sorrows.

CALISTO. The devil go with you!

SEMPRONIO. No, truly, I think he prefers to stay with you! Why, this is a very sudden affliction! What disaster has so quickly robbed my master of his mirth? And, what is worse, of his five wits? Shall I stay with him, or leave him alone? If I leave him, he may kill himself; if I stay, he may kill me! After all, why should I meddle in the matter? Better for him to die, since he hates life, than I, who love it! Even if I desired life for no other reason than to enjoy my Elicia, that would be enough to make me avoid danger. But if he kills himself, with no one else at hand, I shall be answerable for it. I will stay. But even if I do, he won't listen to me. I'll wait and see if he calms down, for it is dangerous to meddle with festering sores before they are ripe. Softly then, let him weep! Tears relieve the overburdened heart. If he sees me here, his wrath may kindle again. I will stay quietly in my corner. If he wants to kill himself, let him! His death may do me a good turn. Yet it is wrong to expect to profit by another's death. Besides, the devil may be tempting me, and his death may be the death of me! Wise men say that it is a great consolation to the afflicted to reveal their griefs; for hidden maladies are the most dangerous. Therefore, instead of havering and wavering, the best thing is to approach him boldly.

CALISTO. Sempronio?

SEMPRONIO. Sir?

CALISTO. Give me my lute!

SEMPRONIO. Here it is, sir!

CALISTO. What grief is there on earth
      Can equal this of mine?

SEMPRONIO. The lute is out of tune.

CALISTO. And how shall I tune it, out of tune as I am? How can I produce sweet harmony? I am out of harmony with myself, my will no longer obeys my reason, the poisoned arrow rankles in my breast. Peace and war, love and hate, injury, fear, and suspicion, battle there for supremacy. Here, take the lute, and sing me the saddest song you know.

SEMPRONIO.   Nero from the Tarpeian rock
               Sees Rome burn, a furnace hot;
               Old and young for succour cry—
               Nero hears, but heeds them not.

CALISTO. Fiercer is the flame that devours me, and less her pity is that kindles it!

SEMPRONIO. (I was right! My master has lost his wits!)

CALISTO. What are you muttering there?

SEMPRONIO. Nothing.

CALISTO. Tell me what you said. Do not be afraid!

SEMPRONIO. I said how can a fire which burns only one person be hotter than that which devours a whole city and a multitude of men?

CALISTO. How? I will tell you. The flame which burns for a hundred years is fiercer than that which is quenched in a day. The fire which destroys one soul is hotter than that which burns a thousand bodies. There is as much difference between the fire you sing of and that which devours me as between appearance and reality, nature and art, shadow and substance. Truly, if the flames of purgatory equal these, I would rather my soul should perish like that of a brute beast than gain paradise by such means!

SEMPRONIO. (This is even worse than I thought! My master is not only mad, but a heretic!)

CALISTO. Did I not tell you to speak up? What are you muttering there?

SEMPRONIO. I said God will not listen to you if you speak heresy.

CALISTO. Why not?

SEMPRONIO. What you have just said goes clean against the Christian religion.

CALISTO. What is that to me?

SEMPRONIO. Are you not a Christian?

CALISTO. I am a Melibean! I adore Melibea, I believe in Melibea, I worship Melibea!

SEMPRONIO. Just listen to him! His heart is so full of Melibea that she comes gushing out of his mouth like water from a spring! Say no more, sir! Now that I know what ails you, I can soon cure it!

CALISTO. Impossible!

SEMPRONIO. Nothing easier! A man is half way to health when his disease is known.

CALISTO. How can you cure one who rejects all counsel and advice?

SEMPRONIO. (Is this the flame that burns Calisto? Is this the cause of all his anguish? As if he were the first to feel love's darts! O Almighty God, how great are Thy mysteries! How high a price is set on love, since all lovers undergo such tribulation! Its bounds are set for men to marvel at, yet lovers ever seek to outstrip them. Like young bulls that feel the prick of darts, they leap, they break away, they overthrow all barriers. God commanded man for woman's sake to leave his father and his mother. Now he does more, for like Calisto he forsakes God Himself. Ah well, saints, wise men, and prophets have done as much!)

CALISTO. Sempronio!

SEMPRONIO. Sir?

CALISTO. Do not leave me!

SEMPRONIO. Now he has changed his tune!

CALISTO. What think you of my malady?

SEMPRONIO. That it comes from loving Melibea.

CALISTO. And nothing else?

B 100

SEMPRONIO. That is bad enough! It is a mistake to put all your eggs in one basket.

CALISTO. You know nothing of constancy.

SEMPRONIO. Constancy? In my country we call it obstinacy and pig-headedness! Victims of Cupid can call it what they will!

CALISTO. How ill it becomes a man to condemn in others what he does himself! Are you not constant to your Elicia?

SEMPRONIO. Do as I say, and not as I do!

CALISTO. What do you reproach me with?

SEMPRONIO. With subjecting the dignity of a man to the weak rule of an imperfect woman.

CALISTO. Woman? Injurious wretch, say Goddess rather!

SEMPRONIO. You are joking!

CALISTO. Joking? No! I believe in Melibea, I worship Melibea, I acknowledge no other deity in heaven while she remains on earth.

SEMPRONIO. Ha, ha, ha! (What blasphemy! What blindness!)

CALISTO. Why do you laugh?

SEMPRONIO. To think that there can be a worse sin than that of Sodom.

CALISTO. What do you mean?

SEMPRONIO. They sinned with unknown angels, but you aspire to one you believe divine!

CALISTO. The devil take you for making me laugh, which I did not think to do to-day!

SEMPRONIO. Do you mean to weep for the rest of your life?

CALISTO. Yes.

SEMPRONIO. Why?

CALISTO. For love of her whom my unworthiness forbids me to approach.

SEMPRONIO. (Oh, the coward! Oh, the miserable son of a

whore!) Why, Nimrod and Alexander the Great thought themselves worthy to reign in heaven as well as on earth!

CALISTO. I cannot hear what you are saying. Speak up, I tell you!

SEMPRONIO. Are you less than Nimrod, or Alexander the Great? Will you despair of obtaining a woman? Why, many of them, and great ladies too, have been ready enough to submit to the embraces of a muleteer, or even of a savage beast. Have you never heard of Pasiphae and the bull, or of Minerva and the dog?

CALISTO. I do not believe such old tales. They are only fables.

SEMPRONIO. And the tale of your grandmother and her monkey? Was that a fable? Witness the knife of your grandfather, that killed the brute!

CALISTO. A curse on your impertinence!

SEMPRONIO. Have I pricked you, sir? Read your historians, study your philosophers, examine your poets! There you will find lewd and villainous examples of lechery, and of the downfall of those who held women in high esteem, as you do. Listen to Solomon, who says that wine and women bring men to ruin; consult Seneca, and you shall see how cheap he holds them; harken to Aristotle, consult St Bernard. Jews, Gentiles, Moors, and Christians all agree on this subject. Yet, whatever I have said or may say of women, do not take it for the whole truth. Some have led virtuous lives, and so escape the general censure. But as for the rest, what shall I say of their lies, their traffickings, their intrigues, their incontinence, their crocodile tears, their impudence, their audacity? What they desire, they do, without hesitation. Who can describe their dissimulation, scandal-mongering, deceit, forgetfulness, unkindness, ingratitude, inconstancy, perfidy, neglect, wantonness, presumption, vanity, baseness, folly, disdain, pride, meanness, gossiping, gluttony, luxury, sluttishness, slyness, boldness, witchcraft, subtlety, mockery, bawdry, effrontery, scurrility? Consider what snares lie beneath their gossamer veils, their starched ruffs, their embroidered robes! What sins, what shames are hidden by their painted faces! Truly have they been called 'weapons of the devil, source of all evil, destroyers of paradise.' Have you not read in the book of the Feast of St John: 'Behold the woman, original sin, for whom Adam threw away the delights of paradise, who dragged mankind down into hell, who was condemned by the prophet Elijah' and so on, and so on?

CALISTO. Why then did Adam, Solomon, David, Aristotle, Virgil, all those whom you mention, submit themselves to women? Am I greater than they?

SEMPRONIO. Be like those who overcame women, not like those who submitted to them! Keep out of their clutches! For it is impossible to understand them. They have no reason, no moderation, no comprehension. They reject what they most desire, insult where they most affect, attract, repulse, summon, dismiss, melt with ardour, burn with hate, soon angry, soon appeased! They would have you guess in advance their most secret desires. Oh, what a plague, what a curse, what a torment it is, to be longer in their toils than the fleeting moments when they give us pleasure!

CALISTO. Yet the more you rail at them, the deeper I fall in love, I know not why!

SEMPRONIO. Then this is not the right medicine for you! You have not learnt to submit to reason, or bridle your desires. It is a sad thing to see one set up for teacher who was never yet schooled!

CALISTO. Who taught you all this?

SEMPRONIO. Why, women, of course! Once they are shamed, they lose all shame. All I have told you, and more, they will reveal to any man. Weigh them with your own honour, think yourself worthier than her you worship! For truly it is worse for a man to rate himself too low than to esteem himself higher than he deserves.

CALISTO. But what can I do?

SEMPRONIO. Consider yourself! You are a man of excellent wit, endowed by nature with many good gifts—beauty, elegance, strength, agility; and above all with a fortune to match. For without money no man can be happy! And finally, you were born under so lucky a star that all men admire you.

CALISTO. Except Melibea! And her qualities, without comparison, far outweigh those that you have praised in me. For consider, Sempronio, her noble and ancient lineage, her immense fortune, her excellent wit, her resplendent virtues, her ineffable grace, her sovereign beauty, of which let me discourse a little for my own refreshment. And I shall speak only of her outward person, for could we discern what is hidden from us, we should not need to continue this miserable argument!

SEMPRONIO. (What lies, what foolishness, will my poor master now be guilty of!)

CALISTO. What are you saying?

SEMPRONIO. I said I shall be happy to listen to you. (God only knows how much I shall enjoy it!)

CALISTO. What's that?

SEMPRONIO. God knows what pleasure I shall take in it!

CALISTO. Then, to prolong your pleasure, I will draw her portrait in detail.

SEMPRONIO. (Fool that I was! I've got more than I bargained for! How long will this wearisome business last?)

CALISTO. I will begin with her hair. You have seen fine gold thread spun in Arabia? Her hair is finer, and shines no less brightly. It flows to her feet, and when she combs it and loops it up in a thousand fantastic knots, her beauty would turn men into stones.

SEMPRONIO. (Or into asses!)

CALISTO.   What do you say?

SEMPRONIO.   I said such hair is not found on an ass's hide.

CALISTO.   Oh, brutish comparison!

SEMPRONIO.   (Are you so wise?)

CALISTO.   Her eyes are large and green, with long lashes and finely arched brows; her nose aquiline, her mouth small, her teeth white and even, her lips red and pouting; her face oval, her bosom high, her breasts round, with small pink nipples— but who can describe them?   A man would run mad but to look on them.   Then her skin, smooth and lustrous as new-fallen snow, the colours mingled as cunningly as if she had chosen them herself!

SEMPRONIO.   (Lord, how the fool runs on!)

CALISTO.   Small hands, soft and yielding, narrow fingers, bright nails like rubies set in pearls!   And those perfections which were hidden from me, to judge by what I saw, must far exceed in beauty the goddess to whom Paris gave the golden apple.

SEMPRONIO.   Have you finished?

CALISTO.   In as few words as possible!

SEMPRONIO.   Even if all this were true, she is still a woman, and therefore inferior.

CALISTO.   How?

SEMPRONIO.   In that she is an imperfect creature—and her fault is to desire you, and others besides.   Have you not read in your philosophies: 'As matter seeks form, so woman seeks man?'

CALISTO.   O unhappy wretch, when shall I see Melibea seek my love?

SEMPRONIO.   Sooner than you expect!   And when you have enjoyed her you will hate her as much as you now desire her, seeing her with other eyes.

CALISTO.   What eyes?

SEMPRONIO.   Clear and unclouded.

CALISTO. How do I see her now?

SEMPRONIO. With dazzled sight, that magnifies her little merit into much! Yet do not despair; I will get you your heart's desire.

CALISTO. God prosper your enterprise! It makes me happy to hear you; yet I have no hope of your success.

SEMPRONIO. I shall certainly succeed!

CALISTO. Heaven help you! That doublet of silk I wore yesterday—Sempronio, it is yours!

SEMPRONIO. God reward you for the gift, and for any others that you may make me! (I shall do well out of this jest! If he pricks me on with such baubles, I'll bring her to his bed. Courage, Sempronio! Such generosity must not go unrewarded!)

CALISTO. Be diligent in this matter.

SEMPRONIO. And you too! For they say a careless master makes a bad servant!

CALISTO. How will you set about it?

SEMPRONIO. Easily! Some time ago I made the acquaintance of a bearded old hag who lives near here, one Celestina, a cunning witch, skilled in all villainies. To my knowledge she has made and unmade five thousand virgins in this city! She could move stones to lechery by her art.

CALISTO. How can I speak with her?

SEMPRONIO. I will go and fetch her. So be ready! Be frank with her, and above all generous! And while I am gone, think over how best to tell her of your malady, for which I am sure she will find a cure.

CALISTO. Go quickly!

SEMPRONIO. I am gone already! God keep you!

CALISTO. And you! O Eternal, Omnipotent Father, who leadest to safety those that stray, who sentest a star to guide the Eastern Kings to Bethlehem and safely home again, humbly I pray Thee, go with my Sempronio, that he may turn my

sorrow into joy, and bring me, all unworthy as I am, to my
desired end!

CELESTINA. Elicia, Elicia, good news, good news! Here
comes Sempronio!

ELICIA. Softly, softly!

CELESTINA. Why, what is the matter?

ELICIA. Crito is here!

CELESTINA. Hide him in the broom cupboard, quick! Tell
him your cousin is here, one of my friends.

ELICIA. Quickly, Crito, hide in here! My cousin is coming.
I shall be lost!

CRITO. Don't worry! I will keep out of sight.

SEMPRONIO. Well, old woman, how glad I am to see you!
Thanks be to God, who led me here again!

CELESTINA. Oh, my pride, my joy—how you startled me!
You quite took my breath away. Come, kiss me—and again!
Three days you haven't been to see us! Elicia, Elicia, here
he is!

ELICIA. Who?

CELESTINA. Why, Sempronio!

ELICIA. Ah, misery! How my heart beats! Where is he?

CELESTINA. Here, with me! I'll have all his kisses if you
don't hurry!

ELICIA. Ah, villain, thrice-accursed villain! The pox take
you, blains and boils light on you! May you fall into the
hands of your enemies, and perish miserably—ah me, ah me!

SEMPRONIO. Why, Elicia, what's the matter?

ELICIA. Three whole days! To stay away from me three
days! God punish you as you deserve! Woe to the wretched
woman who looks to you for happiness!

SEMPRONIO. Softly, sweetheart! Separation cannot quench
my love, or dowse the flame that burns in my heart. Wherever
I am, you are always with me. Don't torment yourself! But
whose footsteps are those I hear overhead?

ELICIA. Those? One of my lovers!

SEMPRONIO. A likely tale!

ELICIA. It's true! Go on, go up, you'll see!

SEMPRONIO. Very well, I will!

CELESTINA. Don't listen to her, Sempronio! She is so upset by your absence, she does not know what she is saying. She'll say anything to tease you. Come and talk to me, and don't waste your time over such foolishness.

SEMPRONIO. Yes, but who is up there?

CELESTINA. Do you really want to know?

SEMPRONIO. Yes.

CELESTINA. A young girl, sent me by the friar.

SEMPRONIO. Which friar?

CELESTINA. Does it matter?

SEMPRONIO. Now, on my life, old woman, which friar?

CELESTINA. Well—the fat friar!

SEMPRONIO. Poor girl! What a burden she'll have to bear!

CELESTINA. Ah, we all come to it! Yet I'll warrant you haven't seen many saddle-sore?

SEMPRONIO. Saddle-sore, no, but badly swollen!

CELESTINA. Fie, mocker!

SEMPRONIO. That's as may be! But—let me see her!

ELICIA. Oh, you villain! So you want to see her? Your eyes are popping out of your head! One woman isn't enough for you, you want them all! Very well, you may see her, but don't come near me again!

SEMPRONIO. Quietly, my dear, don't get excited! I don't want her or anyone else at the moment. I came here to speak to Celestina. So good day to you!

ELICIA. Ungrateful wretch! Very well, go, and stay away three years next time, for all I care!

SEMPRONIO. Now, old lady, trust me. You know I wouldn't make a fool of you. Not a word! Take up your cloak and

come with me.   And on the way I'll tell you something that
may prove profitable to us both.

CELESTINA.   Let us be going!   Elicia, bolt the door behind us,
and good night to you!

SEMPRONIO.   Now, good mother, put everything else out of
your head, and listen to me.   And don't try to think of half a
dozen things at once, or you won't succeed in any of them!
You will never guess what I have to tell you!   It is a secret
that I have wanted to share with you ever since I first heard
it.   See how I trust you!

CELESTINA.   My son, if God were to give you half His kingdom, it would be no more than you deserve for your kindness
to this poor old sinner!   Now tell me everything.   We are
old friends, and there is no need of preambles and circum-
locutions to prove my good faith.   Come, speak briefly and
to the point.   Don't waste two words where one will do.

SEMPRONIO.   Then know, briefly, my master Calisto is madly
in love with Melibea.   He needs our help.   And since he
needs us both, let us both profit by it.   For to take time by the
forelock is a sure way to succeed.

CELESTINA.   Well said, my son!   I understand you well
enough.   I am as glad at this news as a surgeon at a cracked
skull!   And as he begins by probing the wound, to make it
worse and so prolong the cure, I will begin by making Calisto
despair of success, for, as they say: 'Hope deferred maketh
the heart grow sick!'   And the more he suffers the greater his
joy in the end.   You understand me?

SEMPRONIO.   Well enough!   But softly now, here we are at
the door.   And, as they say, walls have ears!

CELESTINA.   Knock then!

SEMPRONIO.   Rat-tat-tat-tat!

CALISTO.   Parmeno!

PARMENO.   Sir?

CALISTO.   Are you deaf, fool?

PARMENO.   What is it, sir?

CALISTO.   See who knocks!

PARMENO.   Who is there?

SEMPRONIO.   Open the door!   It is I, Sempronio, with a lady!

PARMENO.   Sir, it's Sempronio, with a raddled old bawd.

CALISTO.   Mind your manners, you rascal!   The lady is—my
   aunt.   Open the door, quickly!   How often a man, flying
   from one danger, falls into another!   By concealing this affair
   from Parmeno, who through fear or affection serves me well,
   I have risked offending the old woman, who has more power
   over my life than God Himself.

PARMENO.   Why blame me, sir?   Do you think she minds
   what I call her?   Of course not!   She is as proud of it as you
   when they say 'Calisto is a fine horseman!'   She's known as
   a bawd everywhere.   If she were in a whole crowd of women,
   and a passer-by called out 'Ho there, old bawd!' she'd nod
   her head and smile a greeting.   You will find her at all feast-
   ings, junketings, weddings, christenings, and funerals.   Dogs
   bark her name; birds sing it, sheep bleat it, oxen low it: Old
   bawd!   The frogs of the marshes say nothing else;   the
   hammers of the smiths beat it out.   Carpenters and armourers,
   tinsmiths and wool-sorters, fill the air with it.   The carders
   card it, the weavers weave it.   The husbandmen, in the vines,
   in the orchards, in the fields, find her in their daily tasks; the
   gamblers praise her in their losses.   All things glorify her in
   their own tongues.   And if one stone strikes another it says:
   'Old bawd!'

CALISTO.   How do you know all this?

PARMENO.   I'll soon tell you that, sir!   Many years ago my
   poor old mother lived near this Celestina, and, at the old
   woman's earnest entreaties, sent me to be her serving-lad.
   But I stayed with her so short a time, and have since altered
   so much, that she does not recognize me.

CALISTO.   You say you were in her service?

PARMENO. Yes, I went with her to market, carried home her shopping, did everything my puny strength would allow. And although I stayed with her only a short time, I learnt much that I have never forgotten! This old woman had a house by the river, at the other end of the city, near the tanyards. It was in bad condition, poorly patched and worse furnished! She followed half a dozen trades—laundress, perfumer, maker of fards, mender of virginities, a bawd, and a bit of a witch! The first trade covered all the others, and because of it many young servant-girls went to her house, to wash and iron shirts, ruffles, and chemises. And they never arrived without something filched from their mistresses—a piece of ham, a jar of wine, or a bag of flour. The place was full of stolen goods! She was a great friend to young students, and to the stewards and pages of noble houses. To them she sold the innocency of young girls, drawn into her clutches by promise of advancement. She went even further! By means of her spies she penetrated into the most closely guarded houses, and suborned the young daughters to her foul practices. For that she would choose the most sacred moments; under cover of religious processions, early masses, confessions, and hours of prayer, many young women slipped secretly into her house. They were followed by barefoot men, wrapped in cloaks or stripped to the waist, pretended penitents who came to confess their sins. You can imagine what happened then! She appointed herself physician to young children, fetched flax from one house, had it spun in another, and so entered everywhere. Everybody knew her! It was: 'Here, good mother!' 'There, good mother!' 'The old lady!' 'The mistress!' And with all this she never missed mass or vespers, never neglected convent or nunnery, but everywhere mingled her devotions with intrigue. At home she distilled perfumes, fabricated storax, benjamin, myrrh, amber, civet, musk, opoponax, and terebinth. Her room was full of flasks, flacons, and barrels of divers shapes, in glass, earthenware, copper, and tin. She concocted unguents and rouges, washes for the complexion, essences for the bath, waxes, oils, greases, milks, creams, whitening and other paints for the face, of raspings, of roots, of senna pods, of tarragon, of bile, of verjuice, of must, distilled and sweetened. She made skin-foods from the juice of lemons, the lees of wine, the marrow-bones of deer and heron; scented waters with roses, orange-flowers, jasmine, trefoil, honeysuckle, mignonette, pinks and musk-roses, powdered in wine. She made hair-dyes from vine-shoots, oak-leaves, barley, horehound, saltpetre, alum, and a thousand other things. It would be tedious to recall the oils, butters, and greases which she used—from cows, bears, horses, camels, snakes and rabbits, from whales, herons and bitterns, deer, wild-cats and badgers, squirrels, hedgehogs and otters. And it was wonderful to see the herbs and roots which hung from the roof of her house: camomile, rosemary, marsh mallow, maidenhair, melilot, marguerite, elderflower and mustard-seed, lavender, laurel—white, spotted and variegated—mallow and golden-rod, tamarisk and fig-leaves. You would not believe what washes she distilled for the face—from jasmine, lemon, spikenard, violets, benjamin, apple-pips, pine-kernels, pistachio nuts, small seeds of all kinds, fennel, caraway, coriander, lucerne, vetch, and chickweed. In a small phial she kept a precious bit of balm, to heal that sore on her nose. As for maidenheads—some she mended with little bladders, others with a few stitches. In a small painted cupboard she kept a packet of fine furriers' needles, waxed threads of fine silk, and bundles of medicinal herbs; with these she worked miracles! When the French ambassador was here, she sold him one of her servants three times for a virgin!

CALISTO. So she might have done for a hundred others!

PARMENO. Indeed she might! And she mended for charity many poor orphan girls and prostitutes who resorted to her.

In another room she kept love-philtres and potions, made of stags' hearts, vipers' tongues, quails' heads, asses' brains, horse-dung, an infant's caul, barbary beans, seaweed, a hangman's rope, ivy-berries, the quills of a porcupine, a badger's foot, fern-seed, a stone from an eagle's nest, and a hundred other things. Many men and women came secretly to her. From some she took a morsel of bread into which they had bitten, from others a shred of cloth from a garment they had worn, from others a lock of hair. Some she marked in the hand with letters, painted in saffron or vermilion. To some she gave waxen hearts stuck full of broken needles, to others hideous shapes in clay or lead. She drew circles on the ground, she muttered incantations. I cannot tell you all the old witch did! And all of it mockery and lies!

CALISTO. Enough, Parmeno! We will talk of this later. I am glad of your good advice, but we must not keep the old woman waiting. She came here at my request. I am like a drowning man, who snatches at a straw! Let us go! But first promise me, Parmeno, that envy of Sempronio, who has done me great service in this matter, will not make you less eager to help in what may well save my life. I have given him a silken doublet; a silken surcoat shall be yours! For do not think I prize your help less than his. Good counsel takes precedence over bodily labours. Animals work for us, and because of that we house and feed them; but we do not make them our friends. The same distinction I make between you and Sempronio. And between ourselves I may say that, saving my rights as your master, I choose you for my friend.

PARMENO. I am sorry, sir, that you should doubt my loyalty, as your protestations and promises seem to show. When did you see me envious, or neglectful of your service for my own personal profit?

CALISTO. Do not misunderstand me! Your behaviour and good breeding place you, in my eyes, far above all my other servants. But in so difficult a situation, on which my life and happiness depend, we must advance with caution. I know you have an appearance of good nature, but such shows are often put on to trick us. Now, no more! Let us hasten to my salvation.

CELESTINA. I hear footsteps! Someone is coming! Pretend not to notice, Sempronio, and let me do the talking, for the benefit of us both.

SEMPRONIO. Well, talk away!

CELESTINA. Do not vex me with your importunities, Sempronio! You only add to my burdens, and flog a willing horse. I know you feel your master's anguish as much as if it were your own, but, believe me, I have not come here without a remedy! Calisto shall have what he desires, or I will die in the attempt.

CALISTO. Wait, Parmeno, let us hear what they are saying. How do we stand? O excellent woman! All earthly gifts are unworthy of so noble a creature. O faithful and sincere Sempronio! You see, Parmeno, I was right! What do you say, guardian of my secret soul?

PARMENO. First let me again protest my loyalty, and then, since you ask me, I will say what I think. Do not listen to them; do not rush blindly on, for many, seeking the bull's-eye, miss the target. Although I am young, I have seen much, and experience is a good teacher. Hearing you behind the door, they spoke thus on purpose to deceive you. They are raising your hopes with lying promises.

SEMPRONIO. Celestina, Parmeno will ruin all!

CELESTINA. Softly, for by all the saints, when the ass comes the stick follows after! Leave me to deal with Parmeno. I will win him over, by promising to divide with him whatever we get. I will soon have him eating out of my hand, and then we shall be three against one!

CALISTO. Sempronio!

SEMPRONIO. Sir?

CALISTO. Are you there, my most faithful servant? Open at once, Parmeno, he has come back. Oh, I am saved, I breathe again! Welcome to my house, most reverend lady! I see by many outward signs your inward excellence. O virtuous old age, that brings me hope of happiness! I burn to embrace you, but the unworthiness of my person prevents me. Let me kiss the ground you tread on, and do it reverence in your honour.

CELESTINA. (That is all very well, Sempronio, but we cannot live on words alone. Does your fool of a master think I can gnaw the bare bones of a compliment? He's quite mad! Tell him to shut his mouth and open his purse. Fine words butter no parsnips!)

PARMENO. Curses on the old beldame! How true it is that you cannot touch pitch without being defiled! Oh, unhappy Calisto! Now will he bend the knee before the worst whore that ever rubbed shoulders in a brothel! He is undone, he is overthrown, he is fallen away for ever, incapable of speech, of reason, of redemption.

CALISTO. What says the old lady, Parmeno? Does she think I will pay her in words only?

PARMENO. So it appears!

CALISTO. Come, give me my keys! I will soon restore her confidence.

SEMPRONIO. A good move, sir! For doubts in the heart of a friend are like tares among wheat. They must be cut down by the sickle of good deeds.

CALISTO. Well said, Sempronio! Let us go, quickly!

CELESTINA. Parmeno, I am glad to have the chance of a few moments alone with you, for I am very fond of you, little though you deserve it. Yes, I heard what you said just now! But I shall take no notice of it, for religion teaches us to resist temptation, and return good for evil. Particularly when we are vexed by peevish boys who know nothing of the world, and out of a misguided sense of loyalty bring ruin on themselves and their masters! Yes, I heard you! I may be old, but I have not yet lost my hearing—or my other senses! And I can penetrate below the outward show, and see with the eyes of the mind! I would have you know, Parmeno, that Calisto is sick unto death for love of Melibea; but you must not think him weak or foolish because of this. Love invincible vanquishes all men. And learn, if you do not know it already, that there are two things which are always true—first, that man needs woman, and woman man; and second, that he who truly loves must necessarily be troubled and run mad of that sweet passion which the Creator of all things ordained for the propagation of mankind, which else would perish from the earth. And not only human beings obey His law, but birds, beasts, fishes, reptiles, yes, even plants, if placed near each other—for which reason gardeners call some plants male and some female. What do you say to this, Parmeno? My chick, my cherub, my pearl, my little simpleton! Why, pretty fool, you know nothing of the world or its pleasures! Pox take me if I let you come near me, old as I am! You have a broken voice, your beard sprouts! I warrant your manhood can tickle a wench!

PARMENO. Like the tail of a scorpion!

CELESTINA. Worse, worse, mad rogue! For he stings without swelling, but your prick swells nine months.

PARMENO. Ha, ha, ha!

CELESTINA. Do you laugh, shameless creature?

PARMENO. Don't blame me, good mother, nor take me, young as I am, for a fool. I love my master, and he respects me, and that is a great bond between us. I see him beside himself. That is bad enough. But to seek a remedy at the hands of such a brute as Sempronio is lamentable folly. I weep for him.

C 100

CELESTINA. No good, Parmeno! You cannot cure him that way. Besides, others before him have been in like case.

PARMENO. But I hate to see my master suffer.

CELESTINA. He's in no danger! And if he were, I could cure him.

PARMENO. I hope not! For your cure would be worse than the disease!

CELESTINA. Wretched boy, how little you understand what you are saying! Don't you realize what is the matter with him? I tell you he is sick of love, and his cure lies in the hands of this poor old woman.

PARMENO. Say rather this wicked old witch!

CELESTINA. Devil take your impudence! How dare you speak to me so?

PARMENO. Go to, old woman, I know you well enough.

CELESTINA. Who are you?

PARMENO. Parmeno, son of your old friend Alberto! I lived in your house once, down by the river, near the tanyards.

CELESTINA. Sweet Jesu! Are you Parmeno, the son of Claudina?

PARMENO. I am.

CELESTINA. May the flames of hell devour you! Why, your mother was as great a bawd as I! Don't you insult me, boy! Is it really you? By all the saints in heaven, it is! Come here, you rascal! I've given you many a box on the ear, and many a kiss too! Do you remember how you used to sleep at the foot of my bed, you rogue?

PARMENO. Yes, and how you would clasp me in your arms, and try to pull me, young as I was, into your bed! And how I wriggled away, because you smelt of old age.

CELESTINA. A pox on you, insolent! Aren't you ashamed? But, joking apart, you owe me something, Parmeno. For though I was called here on one errand, I came on another. You thought I did not recognize you! But it is really for your sake that I am here. Now listen to me! You know your mother placed you with me, and when you ran away she died of a broken heart. Your bad behaviour, as they say, brought her grey hairs with sorrow to the grave. But before she died she sent for me secretly, and begged me, before heaven that is my witness, to find you and take you back again. And when you reached man's estate, to hand over to you a secret hoard of gold and silver, a fortune greater than Calisto's even! I promised, and she died happy. And since then I have spent much time and money in searching for you. And to-day, by the mercy of God, who ordains all things and answers all prayers, I have been led to this house, where I learned only three days ago that you were lodging! What a pity it is that you should have gone so far, and have so little to show for it! Truly the man who is everywhere is nowhere at home! Nothing is worse for a man than to be continually on the move. The wound never heals that is always reopening, nor can the tree thrive that is often transplanted. Therefore, my son, master the impetuosity of youth, and take the advice of one who loves you. Be reasonable, and settle down. And where better than with me, to whom you were confided by your sainted mother? I speak to you now as if you were my own son, and her curse be on you if you disobey me! I advise you to stay here for the time being, and serve your master well. But go cautiously, and don't try to build a house on sand—for that is all a master's promises are, these days! Make friends with your own kind, and they will be loyal. But do not rely too much on the promises of Calisto, who, like all the rest of such gentry, will pay you with empty phrases, suck you dry as a leech sucks blood, and then turn you off without a penny to bless yourself with! Woe to him who grows old in a prince's service! Masters to-day love themselves better than their servants—and so they should, for the servants do likewise! Liberality, munificence, unselfishness, are out of fashion. It is everyone for himself to-day, and the devil take the hindmost! So we must look after ourselves. I tell you this, Parmeno, because your master strikes me as being a pinchpenny. He seeks to be served without salary! And do not trust too much to his protestations of friendship, for the difference in your positions forbids it. Meanwhile let us make the most of our opportunities. The fortune I told you of shall be well looked after, believe me! For the moment you must stay here, and it would be to your advantage to make a friend of Sempronio.

PARMENO. I am amazed at what I hear. I do not know what to think. I am torn between you, my mother, and Calisto, my master. I should like to be rich, but not by dishonest means. I could not live happily on ill-gotten gains.

CELESTINA. I could! I should like to see my house full to bursting with them!

PARMENO. Then we shall never agree! I hold cheerful poverty to be an honest estate. He who wants little is never poor, he who wants much never rich. I would rather live without envy, sleep without waking, walk in lonely places without fear, bear injury without recrimination, violence without rebellion, and meet oppression with firmness and resolution.

CELESTINA. Oh, my son, how truly they say that you cannot expect old heads on young shoulders! What a child you are!

PARMENO. There is safety in sober poverty.

CELESTINA. Say rather that fortune favours the brave! A rich man never lacks friends. You, thanks be to God, have something in hand, but you need friends to help you keep it. Don't think you'll get rich here! For the more money your master has, the less he will want to part with. And the only remedy against misfortune is good friends. Friendship brings a threefold blessing—companionship, profit, and pleasure.

For companionship you have Sempronio, whose tastes are similar to yours. For profit, it lies in your hands, if you make common cause with him. For pleasure, you are both of an age to enjoy the pastimes of youth—eating, drinking, gaming, jesting, and above all whoring! Oh, Parmeno, what a life we might lead, if you were only willing! For Sempronio is the lover of Elicia, cousin of Areusa.

PARMENO. Of Areusa?

CELESTINA. Yes, Areusa.

PARMENO. Areusa, daughter of Eliso?

CELESTINA. Areusa, daughter of Elisio.

PARMENO. Are you sure?

CELESTINA. Quite sure!

PARMENO. That is very strange!

CELESTINA. Does it please you?

PARMENO. Nothing could please me more!

CELESTINA. Well, if that is what you want, here is someone who is prepared to give it to you!

PARMENO. No, I don't trust you.

CELESTINA. Why not?

PARMENO. I don't trust anyone.

CELESTINA. You would be foolish to trust everyone. But to trust no one is even more foolish!

PARMENO. Well, I will trust you. But it is against my better judgment, believe me!

CELESTINA. Foolish boy! Only a coward fears to venture for his own good. Truly they say: 'The almonds of life come to those who have no teeth!' Oh, you simpleton! The fool has all the luck! Much wit, little money!

PARMENO. I have heard that luxury and avarice are bad teachers. A man should make friends with those who set him a good example, and shun those who seek to corrupt him. I shall not profit by Sempronio's example, nor will mine make him better. And if I take your advice, it must be done secretly.

If a man is overcome by evil, at least he need not undermine the honesty of others.

CELESTINA.   You talk like a fool!   There is no pleasure in wealth without company.   Do not go out of your way to be bitter, and seek solitude, for nature abhors sadness, and seeks delight.   True happiness consists in the sharing of pleasure among friends; especially in affairs of the heart, in recounting and recalling every step of the way: 'I said, she replied, we joked and laughed; I held her so, and thus she kissed me; here she bit me; in this manner I enjoyed her.   How we talked, how we laughed!   How we kissed, how she caressed me!   We came here, we went there, we listened to music, we sang, we rhymed, we played games.   To-day she is going to mass; to-morrow she will walk abroad.   Let us hang round her house; look, here is a message from her; let us visit her by night.   Hold the ladder for me, guard the door!   How did you get away?   Here comes her husband, so she is all alone! To her again; let's in!' and so on, and so on.   And how can you enjoy all that, Parmeno, without a friend?   Tell me that who can?   As for the rest, well, the asses in the field go to it!

PARMENO.   You cannot tempt me with such pleasures, good mother, however much you seek to gild the pill.

CELESTINA.   What pleasures, fool, what pill?   You have no discretion or common sense.   That only comes by experience! And experience is the privilege of old age.   Therefore parents must give good advice to their children, as I do to you.   For above all things I desire your happiness and good fortune. And how will you repay me?   Parents and tutors are never rewarded as they deserve.

PARMENO.   I hesitate to take your advice.   It seems to me rather dubious.

CELESTINA.   You hesitate?   Well, he who hesitates is lost! I will leave you, Parmeno, and have nothing more to do with you.

PARMENO. She is annoyed! I don't trust her, and yet it is only natural that I should want to, especially when she promises me good fortune and success in love! I was taught to obey my elders. What does she want me to do? To make my peace with Sempronio? One should always try to live in peace, for, as they say: 'Blessed are the peacemakers, for they shall be called the children of God!' Love and charity towards one's neighbours is a Christian duty. I should like to keep in with her, if I can. Mother, the old must bear with the ignorance of the young, otherwise we shall never learn. So forgive me, and speak on! I will listen and do what you say.

CELESTINA. There's a sensible lad! Anyone can make a mistake, but to persist in error is a brutish thing. How glad I am, Parmeno, that you have decided to be sensible, and follow the advice of your father, whose memory brings tears to my eyes. He often got odd ideas in his head, just like you, but in the end he always gave in. Upon my soul, seeing you just now, it was as if he were standing before me once again. Oh, what a man he was! So good, so majestic, so venerable! But hush! Here come Calisto and your friend Sempronio. Your friendship with him will soon be profitable to you both, for, as they say, two heads are better than one!

CALISTO. I wondered if I should still find you here. Indeed I am so unhappy that I marvel to find myself still alive. But, good mother, take this poor gift, and my life with it.

CELESTINA. As the goldsmith's art enhances the value of his material, so your present is made more valuable by the sweetness of your liberality! He gives twice who gives quickly, while he seems to regret his promises who is tardy in fulfilling them!

PARMENO. What has he given her, Sempronio?

SEMPRONIO. A hundred pieces of gold.

PARMENO. Alas!

SEMPRONIO. Did the old woman have a word with you?

PARMENO. Yes.

SEMPRONIO. Well, how are we?

PARMENO. Friends, if you wish. I am still amazed.

SEMPRONIO. Don't worry! I'll soon amaze you further!

PARMENO. O God, there is no greater plague than an enemy of one's own household!

CALISTO. Go then, good mother, and settle your affairs. But return soon, and settle mine, I beg of you.

CELESTINA. I will, my son. God be with you!

CALISTO. And with you too. Farewell!

ACT TWO

SUMMARY: *Celestina leaves Calisto and goes home. Calisto talks to Sempronio. Now that he has been given some hope, he feels that matters, however quickly they move, go at a snail's pace. So he sends Sempronio to implore Celestina to carry out her plans quickly. Meanwhile Calisto and Parmeno talk together.*

CALISTO. My friends, I have given the old lady one hundred pieces of gold. Was not that wisely done?

SEMPRONIO. Wisely done indeed, master! For it has improved your situation and enhanced your reputation. And what is the good of wealth, if it does not add lustre to your name? Honour is our chiefest good. It is indeed the reward of virtue, and for that reason we offer it to God, having nothing of greater value to offer Him. And the chief ministers to our honour are liberality and beneficence. Honour is tarnished by avarice, but embellished and rendered more sublime by munificence and generosity. What are great possessions worth, if we do not make use of them? Truly I tell you, the employment of money is more important than the possession of it. How wonderful it is to give, and how miserable to receive! As far as liberality exceeds avarice, so far giving exceeds receiving. Fire, the most generous of all elements, is accounted also the most noble, and takes the first place. They say that nobility is an attribute which comes to us from the merit and ancientry of our ancestors. But such reflected glory never shines as brightly as that which we acquire for ourselves. So do not take pleasure in the nobility of your father, however great, but in your own! Seek honour, the finest attribute of

29

human nature, and one by which good men, like yourself, and not evildoers, come to perfect happiness. Happiness, let me tell you, is not attained merely by good intentions, but by generosity and liberality. And now, sir, take my advice, retire to your room and rest for a while. Your affairs are in good hands, and you may be sure that well begun is half done. Let us go in, for I have still much to say to you on this matter.

CALISTO. No, Sempronio, I do not think I should keep you here while Celestina, who is working so hard for me, is all alone. Go to her, urge her to act quickly! Tell her that on her dispatch depends my safety, on her sloth my sorrow, on her neglect my desolation and despair. You are loyal and affectionate. You are my good and faithful servant. Let her see, if only by your looks, how much I suffer from the flames that devour me. They so parch my tongue and confuse my senses that I cannot tell her half my sufferings. But you, free from such torments, can freely speak of them.

SEMPRONIO. Sir, I am torn in two. I would fly to do your bidding, yet I would also stay here to help ease your pain. Your state alarms me, your solitude bids me remain. But, obedient to your commands, I will go and do what I can to urge the old woman on. And yet, how can I leave you? When you are alone you rave like a madman; sighing, grieving, talking wildly, playing with words, desiring solitude, you find a thousand ways to torment yourself with unhappy thoughts. If you continue thus, you will run mad or die. You need someone with you, to alleviate your sufferings, to joke with you, sing to you, tell you stories, improvise verses, recount anecdotes, play cards, ask riddles—someone, in short, who can devise a thousand pastimes to stop you from brooding over the cruelty with which your lady has received your first avowal of love.

CALISTO. Why, simpleton, do you not know that tears are themselves an antidote to such sufferings? How sweet it is to grieve over the pangs of love! To sigh forth one's soul in sorrow! What comfort lies in tearful groans and cries! All who write of consolation are agreed on that.

SEMPRONIO. Read on, turn the page, and you will see they say also that to trust to time, and to seek cause for sorrow, are equal acts of folly! Even Macías, idol of all lovers, railed against forgetfulness, because he could not forget. The pain of love lies in remembrance; forgetfulness alone brings peace. So do not strive to remember! Feign mirth and pleasure, and soon you will be merry. Let your imagination paint things as you would have them. Though they remain the same in fact, your apprehensions will be calmed and your judgment moderated.

CALISTO. Sempronio, my friend, if you fear to leave me alone, call Parmeno and bid him bear me company. And be always as solicitous for my well-being as you are now! For it is in the affection of his servants that the master finds his best reward. Parmeno!

PARMENO. I am here, sir.

CALISTO. Come where I can see you! Sempronio, stay with Celestina, do not let her forget me. God be with you! Now, Parmeno, what do you think of all this? This waiting is more than I can bear. Melibea is proud; yet Celestina is wise, and past mistress of her art. We cannot fail, you know that in your heart, in spite of your disapproval. I am sure of it! Truth is so strong that it convinces even its enemies. And since Celestina is as you have described her, I would sooner give a hundred pieces of gold to her than five to anyone else.

PARMENO. Are you sure you do not regret it already? (It's a bad business! If there is much more of this generosity, we may all go hungry!)

CALISTO. Since I have asked you for your advice, Parmeno, answer me frankly! Do not hang your head and mutter under your breath. Jealousy is a terrible thing, and should be silent.

Yet it seems to me that you are more occupied with your jealousy than with my unhappiness. What say you, peevish boy?

PARMENO. Sir, I say that you should use your money to buy presents for Melibea, and not give it to the old witch, and, what is worse, become her slave.

CALISTO. How, mad wag, her slave?

PARMENO. You put your liberty into her hands when you share your secrets with her.

CALISTO. You know nothing about it! When—whether by reason of respect and reverence, or of difference in rank, or of reserve and disdain—there is a great gulf fixed between the suppliant and the object of his supplication, as there is between my lady and myself, then a go-between is necessary, to make sure my message reaches the ears of her whom I dare not approach again. And since it must be so, tell me you approve of my employing Celestina!

PARMENO. I would sooner approve of the devil.

CALISTO. What do you mean?

PARMENO. I mean, sir, that mistakes are never made singly. One leads to another.

CALISTO. I agree—but how does that apply to me?

PARMENO. Sir, the loss of your falcon the other day led you to enter Melibea's orchard; entering it, you saw and spoke to her; speaking to her, you fell in love; this love causes your torments; these torments will consume you, body and soul, and waste your fortune; and, what grieves me most of all, you are fallen into the hands of a notorious bawd, who has already been three times in prison.

CALISTO. I am glad you speak so freely, Parmeno. The more you rail against her, the better pleased I am. Once she has served my purpose, they may put her in prison a fourth time, for all I care. But it is easy for you to talk! You do not suffer as I do, Parmeno.

PARMENO. Sir, I would rather you were angry with me now for displeasing you, than reproach me later with not having given you good advice. You have thrown away your freedom in thus giving in to your infatuation.

CALISTO. Do you want a whipping, rogue? Tell me, you ungrateful slave, why you speak evil of her whom I adore? What do you know of honour? Tell me, what is love? Tell me even what constitutes good service, since you pretend to be so clever! Do you not know that the first sign of madness is to believe oneself wise? If you had any feeling for me at all you would find means to soothe the sharp prick of Cupid's dart. Sempronio is wearing himself out in my service, but you only inflame my wound with your cruel words. You protest your loyalty in flattering phrases, but your tongue speaks nothing but lies. You are full of malice and uncharitableness, and just for the sake of slandering a poor old woman you try to discourage my passion. Yet you know quite well that my suffering and my unstable sorrow cannot be ruled by reason, counsel, or good advice. My grief lies so deep that he who would take it from me must first tear out my heart. Sempronio was reluctant to go and leave you here. I forced him to obey, and now suffer the pain of his absence and your company. Truly it is better to be alone than in the presence of one's enemy!

PARMENO. Sir, it is a poor loyalty which fear can convert to flattery, above all to a master deprived by grief of his better judgment. The mists which blind you will disperse, the momentary fire will die down, and then you will realize that my harsh words do you more good than the smooth comfort of Sempronio. That only feeds the flame of your desire, excites your passions, irritates your sorrows, and adds fuel to the fire which will consume you until it lays you in the grave.

CALISTO. Silence, miserable creature! I suffer, and you talk philosophy! I will hear no more. Fetch my horse, brush him well, saddle him richly, and I will ride to the house of my lady, my divinity!

PARMENO. Ho there, a groom! There's not a servant in the house! I must do it myself. Well, I never thought to turn stable-boy! But needs must. . . . So my friend doesn't like it when I speak the truth! You whinny, Sir Horse! Haven't we enough with one lover in the family? Are you in Melibea's power too?

CALISTO. Where is my horse? What are you doing, Parmeno?

PARMENO. Here he is, sir. Your groom was not to be found.

CALISTO. Hold my stirrup, open the gates, and if Sempronio comes with the old woman, tell them to wait; I shall be back soon.

PARMENO. More's the pity! To the devil with him! Tell a fool the truth, and he can't bear the sight of you! Upon my soul, if someone were to thrust a lance into my master's heel, more brains would come out than from his head. Trust me, sir, Celestina and Sempronio will soon bleed you white! They won't stop till they have the shirt off your back! What a fool I am! My virtues are of little account; I am blamed for my loyalty, while others profit by their wickedness. Since the world wags so, I will do likewise. Traitors are now called discreet, and honest men imbeciles. If I had believed Celestina in all the wickedness of her threescore years and ten, Calisto would not have so miscalled me. Let this be a lesson to me in dealing with him hereafter. If he says eat, we'll eat; pull the house down, we'll pull it down; burn it, we'll fetch the fire. Let him wreak havoc, destruction, and damage! Let him waste his substance on old bawds, and I'll take my share! For, as they say, there's good fishing in troubled waters, and the wise man profits by another's folly!

ACT THREE

SUMMARY: *Sempronio goes to Celestina's house and reproaches her for her tardiness. They discuss the best way of conducting Calisto's affair with Melibea. Elicia enters, and Celestina goes to the house of Pleberio; Sempronio and Elicia remain alone together.*

SEMPRONIO. The old woman's taking her time! She moved faster than this on her way to Calisto. But when the money is paid, the work is neglected! Hola there! Celestina! Open the door, I am in a hurry!

CELESTINA. What is it you want, my son?

SEMPRONIO. Our poor invalid is in despair! He doesn't know what to do with himself. Nothing goes right for him. He is afraid you have forgotten him, curses his avarice and meanness, and thinks he didn't give you a big enough bribe!

CELESTINA. Young men in love are always impatient. They are tormented by the slightest delay, and any obstacle enrages them. They expect to attain their ends immediately. They want results without having worked for them. And this is particularly true of a new lover, like your master, who, without a moment's hesitation, gives way to every passing whim, without thinking of the harm he may do to those who serve him!

SEMPRONIO. Harm to those who serve him? Do you think we are in danger of being burnt to cinders by the fire that devours Calisto? I'd send his affairs to the devil before I'd risk that! At the first hint of trouble I shall be off, I assure you! I would rather lose my place than risk my life in trying to keep it. But time will show! At least I hope it will give some warning, like a house before it falls. Good mother, let us not run ourselves into danger! There is no hurry! If we do not succeed this year, we may next. If not then, then some time. If not some time, then never! For there is nothing so difficult at first that time does not eventually make it tolerable and easy; no plague so sore that time does not soften it, no pleasure so acute that time does not blunt it; good and evil, prosperity and adversity, success and failure, all lose their full force with the passing of time. What one has ardently desired and joyfully attained is at last forgotten as if it had never been. Every day we see and hear new things, we tire of them, we leave them behind. Time diminishes them and makes them contemptible. If something terrible happens to you—an earthquake, for instance—you are amazed; but you soon forget all about it. If they say: The river is frozen over, the blind man can see, your father is dead, the lightning has struck, Granada is taken, the king comes to-day, the Turks are vanquished, there was an eclipse this morning, the bridge is broken down, there is a new bishop, Pedro has been robbed, Inez has hanged herself, it is a nine days' wonder! But hear the news a second time, and it no longer interests you. So with everything! It passes, it disappears, it is forgotten! And so it will be with this passion of my master's! The longer it lasts the more easily he will endure it. Custom makes all pain bearable, diminishes all pleasure, cheapens all marvels. So let us profit by it! If we can strike while the iron is hot, so much the better. If not, Melibea's pride will soon abate. And, believe me, I would rather see the master suffer than the servant in danger!

CELESTINA. Well said, my son, I agree with you entirely! Your idea is a sensible one, and we can't go far wrong if we follow it. All the same, you know, a good attorney is careful always to seem busy. He runs many little errands, performs many little tasks, appears frequently in the courts, even at the risk of a rebuke from the judge, so that all who see him may say he earns his fees! And then they want him to plead their cause, just as all lovers want Celestina to plead theirs!

SEMPRONIO. Well, do as you please. This will not be the first time you have been in charge of such a suit!

CELESTINA. The first, my son? No, indeed! Not many young women have set up shop in this city, thank God, without giving me a commission on their first customer! Every girl-child born here is entered on my register, for I like to know how many escape my clutches! Why, Sempronio, how do you think I earn my daily bread? Can I live on air? Am I an heiress? Have I houses and vineyards? Or any other means of livelihood—to get me food and drink, and to keep me clothed and shod? I was born in this city, I grew up here, and here I have lived honestly, as all the world knows. Certainly I am no stranger here! If anyone asks my name or the number of my house, you can be sure he is not a native of our town!

SEMPRONIO. Tell me, mother, what passed between you and Parmeno while I went with Calisto to fetch the money?

CELESTINA. I gave him a good talking to, and told him he would profit more from our company than from all the flattering lies he told his master! That he would always be poor and of little account if he didn't change his way of life, and that he was foolish to act the saint with an old woman like me! I reminded him what his mother was, and told him to change his tune, for if he spoke vilely of me he was attacking her too.

SEMPRONIO. Why, how long have you known him, mother?

CELESTINA. I was there when he was born! I heard his first cry. His mother and I were one flesh. I learned all I know from her. We lived, ate, and slept together, and took in common our pleasures, our decisions, and our resolutions.

D 100

At home and abroad we were like sisters. I never earned a penny without she had her share. I should be a happier woman to-day if she were still here. O death, death, how you take from us all our dear companions! How many you make desolate by your visitations! For one you take at the right time, you cut off thousands too soon. If she had lived I should not walk alone and friendless. May she rest in peace, for she was a true friend and a good comrade to me! I never did anything without her. If I bought the bread, she bought the meat. If I laid the table, she spread the cloth. She was no fool or prude, like the women of to-day. Upon my soul, she could walk barefaced to the other end of the town, her wine jug in her hand, and no one said anything worse to her than 'Madam Claudina!' There was never a better judge of wine, or of any other merchandise! And so quick! While I thought she was on her way out, she was back again! She was invited everywhere, everyone was proud to know her, and she never came home without having tasted a dozen dainty dishes, carrying a measure of wine in her jug and another in her stomach! Her credit was as good in half a dozen shops as if she had pledged them a silver chalice! Her word was worth a gold piece in all the taverns! If we were walking the streets and felt thirsty, we went into the nearest inn, and in a moment we were washing the dust from our throats with a good stoup of liquor. And not a penny to pay! It was chalked up to her, and off we went! I promise you, if her son is anything like her, Calisto won't have a penny left to bless himself with, and we shall get all we want! I'll soon have him under my thumb, and then we shall see!

SEMPRONIO. How will you do that? He's a slippery customer.

CELESTINA. We shall be two to one! I'll give him his Areusa, and then he'll be one of us, trust me! He'll help us lay snares for the gold pieces of Calisto!

SEMPRONIO. Do you really think you can succeed with
Melibea? Have you decided how to set about it?

CELESTINA. No doctor can tell at a glance the full extent of
an injury! But I will tell you what I have seen so far.
Melibea is beautiful; Calisto is madly in love and open-
handed. He will not mind how much money he spends, nor
I how much trouble I take to help him spend it. With money
the affair can drag out as long as it pleases, for money is all-
powerful. It can move mountains or dry up rivers. There
is no place so remote that an ass laden with gold cannot reach
it. Calisto's folly and fury will ruin him, to our profit. That
is what I see! I know what they are, both of them, and we can
benefit by it. Now I am going to Pleberio's house. Don't
worry! Melibea may be proud, but she's not the first I have
humbled, thanks be to God! They are all shy fillies, but once
they have borne the saddle on their backs they don't want to
shake it off! The battle is on for good; they would rather die
than give in! They travel by night, hoping the day will never
come. They curse the cocks that announce it and the clocks
because they tick too fast. They watch the Pleiades and the
North Star; they are all astrologers! When dawn breaks their
hearts break too, for its brightness darkens their joy. I have
travelled the same way, my son! I never tire of it, and old as
I am I thank God I can still enjoy it! So judge how much
more they enjoy it, who travel that way for the first time,
burning with desire, caught in the toils of love! They implore
those who implored them, suffer with those they made suffer,
become the slaves of those who were their slaves, take orders
from those they commanded! Now they will break down
walls, burst open windows, feign maladies, oil the creaking
hinges of the door so that they may work noiselessly! I cannot tell you what strength they draw from the first kisses of him
they love. They are enemies of moderation, and run to
extremes in everything.

SEMPRONIO. I don't understand you, mother.

CELESTINA. I tell you, a woman either hates or adores the man who desires her. And if her love be rejected, it turns to hate! Knowing this, I can approach Melibea with as much confidence as if I had her already under my thumb. For though I must now go on my knees to her, she will soon be begging for my help; though she may send me away now, later she will ask me to return. In my pocket I have a little yarn and a few trifles that make it easy for me to gain admittance into houses where I am unknown—things like lace collarettes, net ruffles, fringes, tuckers, tweezers, spirits of wine, white lead, rouge, pins and needles! While they choose what they want, I chatter, chatter, and decide whether to bait the hook cunningly or speak out plainly and at once.

SEMPRONIO. Old woman, think well what you are doing! A bad beginning makes a bad end. Her father is a great nobleman, her mother virtuous and vigilant; already she suspects you. Melibea is their only child. If they lose her they lose their all. I shudder to think what may happen! Remember the proverb: In going to shear, come not back shorn.

CELESTINA. Shorn, my son?

SEMPRONIO. You may find yourself in prison.

CELESTINA. The devil take you! Do you think I need your advice? Do you presume to teach Celestina her business? Teach your grandmother to suck eggs! I was eating the bread of experience when you were in your cradle! You'd make a fine soldier, with your craven fears and terrors!

SEMPRONIO. Why should you be surprised at me, good mother? It is only natural for a man to be afraid of failing in an enterprise he has set his heart on—and I am afraid we shall both lose our labour! All I want is for this business to end well, not for my master's sake, but to put me beyond the reach of poverty. And since I lack experience, I see the difficulty of our task more than you who are mistress of your trade.

ELICIA. Sempronio! Wonders will never cease! What, you here twice in one day?

CELESTINA. Quiet, rattlepate! Leave us alone, we have something important to discuss. Tell me, is the room empty? Has she gone, that girl who was waiting for the fat friar?

ELICIA. Yes, and the other who came after her—she's gone too!

CELESTINA. I hope she didn't come in vain?

ELICIA. No, no, God forbid! She was late, but, as they say, better late than never!

CELESTINA. Run up to the loft over the gallery, my dear, and bring me down the bottle of serpent's oil that you will find there, tied up with a hempen cord; the one I brought back from the country the night it was raining and black as ink. And open the linen chest, and on the right you will see a paper written in bat's blood, underneath that dragon's wing we pulled the claws from the other day. Take care not to spill the Mayday dew for my lotion!

ELICIA. Mother, the paper is not here; you never know where anything is!

CELESTINA. For heaven's sake, Elicia, have pity on my grey hairs! Don't shout at me like that and scold me so! You're so impatient! And you needn't be so proud, just because Sempronio is here. He would rather have my good counsel than your kisses, although you love him so much! Go into the room where the ointments are—you'll find it wrapped in that black catskin where I told you to put the she-wolf's eyes. And bring down the he-goat's blood and the hairs you clipped from his beard.

ELICIA. Here you are, mother, they're all here! I am going upstairs again. Sempronio, come with me!

CELESTINA. I conjure you, dread Pluto, lord of the infernal regions, emperor of the damned, proud captain of the fallen angels, lord of the sulphurous fires which burn in the caverns of Etna, master and devisor of all torments, executioner of sinful souls, governor of the three Furies, Tisiphone, Megaera, and Alecto, king of the black river of the Styx, of its depths, lagoons, and everlasting chaos, chief of the winged harpies, and of all the company of hideous and many-headed hydras; I, Celestina, known to you these many years, conjure you by the force and virtue of these scarlet letters, by the blood of the night-bird in which they are written, by the power of the words and signs upon this paper, by the black venom of the viper from which this oil was made, and with which this cord is saturated—come without delay and obey my commands! Bind yourself with this cord and from it never depart until Melibea in an auspicious moment takes it from me! May she be so bewitched by it that the more she views it the more her heart may incline towards my petition! May it burn her with the flame that devours Calisto, so that she may throw off all restraint of modesty and yield herself to me, in recompense of all my trials and tribulations! This done, ask of me what you will! Appear at once, or count me your mortal enemy! I will flood with heavenly light your dark and miserable prisons, I will denounce publicly your continual lies, I will threaten with harsh words your dreadful name! Again, and once again, I conjure you! And now, confident in my great powers, I bear away this cord, knowing that you are with me!

ACT FOUR

SUMMARY: *Celestina hurries through the streets, muttering to herself as she goes. Arriving at Pleberio's house, she talks to Lucretia, Melibea's maid. Alisa, Melibea's mother, hears them talking, and on being told that Celestina is at the door, gives orders for her to be brought in. A messenger comes to speak to Alisa, who goes out with him. Celestina remains alone with Melibea, and explains the reason for her visit.*

CELESTINA. Now I am alone I can think over what Sempronio said. He is frightened by my audacity! Indeed such an enterprise, undertaken without due consideration, might end happily, but would be more likely to lead to disaster. However, careful preparation bears good fruit! Although I did not say so to Sempronio, I don't doubt that if the reason for my visit to Melibea were known I should pay for it with my life. Or, even if my life were spared, I should suffer some punishment, and be whipped or tossed in a blanket. Much good my gold pieces would do me then! Unhappy wretch that I am! What a pit I am fallen into! I wanted to appear helpful, and I have staked my life on a hazard. What shall I do, poor miserable creature! To turn back is as dangerous as to go on. Shall I go on? Shall I turn back? Oh, hard and uncertain perplexity! I do not know what to do for the best. I see the dangers that confront me, but if I turn back I am lost indeed! Like a beast of burden I must labour to live. Both roads are blocked by innumerable obstacles. If I am taken red-handed I shall be killed or thrown into prison. If I return home what will Sempronio say? That that is all

43

my courage and cunning were worth, that is all my wisdom
and sagacity were equal to! And his master, Calisto? What
will he say or do? He will think I have broken my promise
and betrayed him, either from malice or spite, or tempted by
a bribe from his enemies. Even if he does not think evil of
me he will rave like a madman, insult me, be furious at the
delay caused by my indecision, say to me: 'Old hag, why did
you raise my hopes with promise of success? False whore,
for others you have winged heels, for me only a lying tongue;
for others action, for me only words; for others a remedy, for
me increase of pain; for others zeal, for me indifference;
for others light, for me darkness! Why, treacherous woman,
did you offer me your help? You gave me hope and fresh
courage, brought me back to life, made me a happy man!
You have failed in your promises. But you shall suffer for it,
as I do!' Alas, alas! Evil on both sides; trouble either way!
When there is no middle course the wise man chooses the
lesser of two evils. I would rather fall foul of Pleberio than
Calisto! Therefore, go on! I will run the risk of keeping
my promise rather than the shame of being called a coward.
And may good fortune go with me! Ah, there's the house.
Well, I have been in worse situations than this. Courage,
good Celestina, don't weaken now! There are always those
who will intercede for the evildoer! Besides, the omens are
favourable or I am much mistaken! Of the four men I have
met, three were called Juan and two were cuckold; the first
word I heard in the street was a word of love; I have not once
stumbled as I do at other times; the very stones seemed to
divide and let me pass; nothing has caught my skirts; I am
not wearied by my long walk; everyone has greeted me; no
dog has barked at me; I haven't seen a black bird or thrush,
not even a crow, no bird of ill omen, and best of all I see
Lucretia, Elicia's cousin, at the door of Melibea's house. She
won't be much of a hindrance to me!

LUCRETIA. Who's that old hag who comes shuffling along here?

CELESTINA. Peace to this house!

LUCRETIA. Ah, Celestina, mother, you are welcome! But what brings you here? We don't often see you in these parts.

CELESTINA. Ah, my daughter, my little darling! It's because I so longed to see you! I bring you greetings from your cousin, Elicia, and I hope to see your mistresses, the young and the old, for I haven't seen hair or hide of them since I moved away from here!

LUCRETIA. And is that all you came for? You surprise me, for it's not like you! I have never known you stir abroad without good reason.

CELESTINA. And what better reason, my silly one, than because I want to? Besides, like all poor old souls, I lack the necessities of life, especially as I have to keep other people's daughters! So I thought I might profit by the occasion to sell some of my yarn.

LUCRETIA. So I was right after all! I am not such a fool as you think! I've seen you throw a sprat to catch a mackerel before this! But you're in luck! My old mistress is weaving and needs more yarn; you have it. So come inside and wait! You may be able to do business with her.

ALISA. Who is there, Lucretia?

LUCRETIA. Madam, the old woman with the scarred face. You know, the one who used to live near the tannery by the river.

ALISA. No, I don't know! What is the good of describing someone I don't know by something I know even less? You might as well fetch water in a sieve!

LUCRETIA. Lord, madam, everyone knows this old woman! It's the one that was put in the stocks for a witch, and for selling young girls to the fat friars, and unmaking a thousand marriages!

ALISA. What trade does she follow? I may remember her by
that.

LUCRETIA. Why, madam, she sells perfumes, paints, powders,
and a thousand other things. She is skilled with herbs, and
cures children, and they call her the old lapidary.

ALISA. None of this helps me to recognize her. Why don't
you tell me her name if you know it?

LUCRETIA. If I know it, madam? Everyone in the city knows
it, from the oldest to the youngest. So why shouldn't I?

ALISA. Then why don't you tell me?

LUCRETIA. I'm ashamed to!

ALISA. Get along with you, you silly girl! You make me
cross with all this nonsense!

LUCRETIA. Then, with all due respect, madam, her name is
Celestina!

ALISA. Ha, ha, ha! You foolish creature, I can't help
laughing at you! You certainly must hate the poor old
woman if you won't even pronounce her name! Yes, of
course, I remember her! A good old soul! Say no more!
I expect she comes on some errand or other. Tell her to
come up!

LUCRETIA. Come up, good mother!

CELESTINA. Gracious lady, God be with you, and with your
noble daughter! My age and my infirmities stop me from
visiting your house as often as I should like to. But God
knows how often I think of you both and the great love I
bear you. Distance is no bar to the heart's affection. And
now necessity drives me to do the very thing I long to. Misery
and misfortune have come upon me, and I am penniless. All
I have to sell is a little yarn that I have spun for a cloth I was
weaving. I hear from your maid that you need some; poor
as I am, I have brought it for you. Here it is! Dispose of
it, and of me, as you wish!

ALISA. Good neighbour, you move me to tears! If it will

relieve your misery I will accept your offer, though I am loth
to spoil your cloth. But we must do what is best! If the
thread is good you shall be well paid.

CELESTINA. Good, madam? I hope my life and my old age,
yes, and that of those who hear me, may be as good! It is as
fine as the hairs on your head, as smooth and strong as the
strings of a guitar, as white as a snowflake! I spun it myself,
and wound it and dressed it. Here it is, all ready, wound in
small skeins, and as I hope for salvation, yesterday I was paid
for this same yarn three silver pieces an ounce.

ALISA. Daughter Melibea, look after this old woman! It is
high time I went to see my sister, Cremes's wife, for I have not
been there since last night, and her page has just come with a
message to say she is much worse.

CELESTINA. The devil does well to make her worse at such a
moment! Go on, good friend, hold fast! It's now or never!
Get the old mother out of the way!

ALISA. What are you saying, my friend?

CELESTINA. Madam, I curse the devil and all my sins that
your sister should be taken ill at such a moment, for then we
shall have no time to conclude our little affair! What is the
matter with her?

ALISA. A pain in the side so terrible that, according to what
her page says, I fear it may prove fatal! Pray for her, neighbour, for the love of God; remember her always in your
prayers!

CELESTINA. Indeed I will, good madam! As soon as I leave
here I will go to all the nunneries where I have good friends,
and I will ask for their prayers too! And before I eat another
morsel I will tell my beads four times over!

ALISA. Come, Melibea, pay the old woman for her thread!
And now, mother, forgive me if I leave you! Another day
we will talk at our leisure.

CELESTINA. Lady, there is no need to ask for my forgiveness, for you leave me in good hands. And may she ever be as young and lovely as she is at present! Youth is the season of pleasure and delight. Old age, believe me, is nothing but a time of infirmities, harbinger of sad thoughts and unhappy memories, a continual anguish, an incurable wound, an ever-present pain, full of regrets for the past, anxieties for the present, dire forebodings for the future, near neighbour of death, a roofless hovel where the rain drips in, a staff of osier which bends under the lightest burden, a broken reed!

MELIBEA. Why do you speak ill, mother, of something all men desire?

CELESTINA. They do not know what they desire! They look forward to old age because it comes by living, and life is sweet. And in living it one grows old! The child longs to be a man, the man looks forward to a ripe old age, and the old man, however infirm, still wants to live a few more years! They all want to live, for, as they say: 'While there's life there's hope!' But I can tell you, lady, the troubles of old age—its dangers, its inconveniences, its fatigues, its fears, its infirmities, its cold, its heat, its discontent, its quarrels, its afflictions! And then its wrinkles, its grey hairs, its deafness, its blindness, its sunken eyes, its hollow cheeks, its toothlessness, its loss of strength, its feeble walk, its slowness in eating! Alas, alas, dear lady, and if with all this poverty comes too, then all other sorrows shrink to nothing! The appetite may remain, but food is lacking! I never had worse indigestion than from hunger.

MELIBEA. You speak of old age as you find it. Perhaps the rich tell another tale.

CELESTINA. Dear child, to each his own bitterness! The rich man's youth slips away imperceptibly, for he is surrounded by flatterers. He only is rich who has made his peace with heaven. It is better to be despised than feared; the poor man sleeps easier than he who must guard anxiously what he has laboured to gain and would grieve to lose. My friends do not flatter me as the rich man's do. I am loved for myself and he for his money. He never hears the truth, for he is surrounded by jealousy and deceit. What rich man would not confess himself happier in obscurity and honest poverty? Possessions do not make you rich—they merely occupy your time. You are not their master, but their servant. More people are owned by their possessions than own them. To many they have brought death, from all they take away pleasure, and nothing is more fatal to the good life than the possession of great wealth. The rich man sleeps, and when he wakes his hands are empty! Every rich man has a dozen sons and grandsons whose only prayer is that he may speedily be taken from them! The hour of his death never comes too soon for them! They lay hands on his money, and hurry him to his eternal resting-place as cheaply as possible.

MELIBEA. Tell me, mother, since you grieve so for the time that is past, would you like to be young again?

CELESTINA. The traveller fatigued by his journey would be mad to start again, just to arrive where he already is! Unpleasant things are better had than anticipated, for then they are sooner over. There is nothing more agreeable than the inn to a tired traveller. Youth is a precious thing, but the wise man knows when it is over. Only a fool hankers after what is gone for ever!

MELIBEA. But surely one may be glad of one's youth and strength, for then one has longer to live?

CELESTINA. Ah, lady, the lamb goes to the slaughter as well as the old ewe! No one is so old that he cannot live another year, nor so young that he cannot die to-day. You have no advantage over me there!

MELIBEA. What you say amazes me. But your conversation reminds me that I have seen you before. Tell me, good mother, are you not that Celestina who lived near the tannery by the river?

CELESTINA.   I am, as long as God pleases!

MELIBEA.   How you have aged!   Truly they say time takes toll of all!   On my life, I would not have known you but for that scar on your face.   I thought you were beautiful once, but now I see I was mistaken.   You are much altered!

LUCRETIA.   Ha, ha, ha!   She must indeed have altered! What, beautiful?   With that great scar on her face?

MELIBEA.   What is the matter with you, girl?   What are you saying?   Why are you laughing?

LUCRETIA.   To think you didn't recognize Celestina!

CELESTINA.   Madam, if you can make time stand still I will keep my face unchanged.   Have you not heard it said: 'The day will come when you look in the mirror and no longer recognize yourself'?   All the same, my hair is prematurely white, and I know I look twice my age, for as sure as you are beautiful and I am an old sinner, I was the youngest of my mother's four daughters.   So I am not as old as you think.

MELIBEA.   Friend Celestina, I am glad to have met you again. Your conversation is most interesting.   Here is your money! Take it, and go, and God be with you!   Have you had anything to eat to-day?

CELESTINA.   Oh, my angelic child, my precious pearl!   How well you talk!   How happy I am just to listen to you!   Do you not remember that God said to the Tempter: 'Man shall not live by bread alone'?   Truly food is not our only sustenance!   I often go days without eating when I am busy about the affairs of others.   I seek salvation in the service of good men.   I would gladly die for them, for I have always thought it better to wear out than rust out.   And now, if you will allow me, I will tell you the real reason for my visit.   You have not heard it yet, and all will be lost if I go without mentioning it.

MELIBEA.   Speak, mother, tell me what you lack and I will do what I can for you, in memory of the days when you were our neighbour.   For we must always help our neighbours.

CELESTINA.   What I lack, lady?   No, it is not for myself I ask anything, but for others, as I told you.   I need little enough.   I leave my troubles at home.   I eat when I can, drink what I have, and for all my poverty I thank God I have never yet lacked a penny for bread and four for wine, since I was widowed.   Before that I never had to worry.   There was always a wineskin in my house, one full and the other empty, and I never went to bed without a sup of wine, for my stomach's sake!   Now that I am alone they bring it in a little jug which hardly holds half a glass, a plague on them!   Old as I am, I have to take my white hairs to the tavern ten times a day, to refill it.   But before I die I hope to see a wineskin in my house again, or at least a good big wine-jar!   To my mind there is no better provision, for, as they say: 'On bread and wine a man goes a long way.'   But when there is no man in the house everything goes awry.   As they say: 'There's no luck about the house when the good man's away.'   But all this comes from my saying it was others who needed your help, not I!

MELIBEA.   Ask what you will, for whoever it may be.

CELESTINA.   Noble lady, the kindness you have shown me gives me courage to speak out.   I come from one who is very near death, and who is so persuaded of your virtue that he believes a word from you would cure him.

MELIBEA.   Old woman, what do you mean?   You must explain yourself more clearly.   Sometimes you disgust me, at others I am moved to pity you.   How can I do what you ask when I do not understand what you want?   I should be happy if any word of mine could save a Christian soul.   To do good is a divine attribute, and the benefit is doubled when it is done to one who merits it.   And he who can save another's life and does not is guilty of his death.   Therefore speak out, without fear or hesitation!

CELESTINA. I lost all fear, dear mistress, on beholding your
beautiful face. I cannot think that God gave you such
surpassing beauty, such grace, such perfection, without giving
you also the virtues of pity and compassion, ministers of His
grace and mercy. Since all men are born to die, no one should
live for himself alone, otherwise we should be like the beasts
that perish. And even among them some are virtuous. The
unicorn is subject to the young virgin, and the dog, with all
his impetuosity and courage, will not bite the hand that feeds
him. Among the birds too the cock summons his hens to
share his food, the pelican tears his breast to nourish his
young, the stork feeds the old birds in the nest where they fed
him. Since Nature gives so much intelligence to birds and
beasts, why should man alone be cruel? Why should we not
give something of ourselves to our neighbour? Above all
when he suffers from a wound whose remedy lies with her who
first inflicted it.

MELIBEA. Before God, tell me, without more ado, who is it
that suffers so, and of so strange a malady that its pain and
its remedy come from the same source?

CELESTINA. Madam, you must have heard tell of a young
gentleman of this town, a noble youth, well born, called
Calisto?

MELIBEA. Stop, stop! Good woman, say no more! Go no
further! Is Calisto the sick man for whom you seek my help?
Did you risk your life here for Calisto? Was it for him that
you came on such a damnable errand? Shameless creature!
What ails him that you should come in such haste? Folly is
his only complaint! If I had not known already of his
wickedness, how easily your words might have led me astray!
Truly they say that the tongue is the most unruly member in
evil man or woman! Witch, bawd, traitor to your sex,
corruptor of youth, enemy of honesty, may you be burnt
alive! Out of my sight! Jesu, Jesu! I am dead, Lucretia!

There is not a drop of blood left in my body! I deserve to be punished for having listened to her! Truly, if I were not afraid for my reputation, I would publicly proclaim the effrontery of this infamous creature. Damnable hag, I would you might be struck dead for having spoken to me thus!

CELESTINA. (I came here in an unlucky hour, if my spell fails me! Alas, I spoke too soon! Brother devil, all is lost!)

MELIBEA. Do you mutter under your breath to enrage me, and so make your punishment the greater? Would you sacrifice my honour to save the life of a madman? Would you bring me to sorrow to pleasure him? Do you hope to profit by my shame, and be rewarded for my errors? Shall my father's house be destroyed and his honour dragged in the gutter to enrich an old hag like you? Do you think I cannot guess your errand, and understand your damnable purpose? I promise you, my answer will prevent your offending further, for you shall not escape alive. Answer me, traitress! How dare you do such a thing?

CELESTINA. Madam, the terror I am in prevents me from justifying myself. My innocence sustains me, but I am distressed to see you so angry. Above all I suffer from a harshness which I have not deserved. Before God, good lady, let me finish what I have to say, and you will see I am not guilty nor blamable! Truly I came in the service of God, not in dishonourable fashion. I was more concerned with the recovery of my patient than with the honour of his doctor. If I had thought, lady, that you would so easily suspect me of unspeakable horrors, I would never have dared, for all your coaxing, to speak to you of Calisto or of any other man!

MELIBEA. Sweet Jesu, let me hear no more of that madman, that night wanderer, that climber of walls, with legs as long as a stork, painted like a popinjay, or I shall die of shame! It was he who accosted me the other day, and heaped idle compliments on me with a great air of gallantry. Tell him, old woman, that if he thinks himself the victor in our encounter, because I listened to his nonsense and did not punish him on the spot for his audacity, it was because I preferred to think him mad rather than publish his disgrace. Advise him to give up his pretensions and regain his sanity. If not he may find the price of his words to me more than he can pay! No one is defeated unless he thinks himself so, and I keep my constancy as well as my pride. Madmen think all the world as mad as they! Go, take back the message you were charged with! Tell him he shall have no other reply from me. He will do well not to expect it. It is useless to sue to one who is pitiless. And give thanks to God that you leave here alive. I know all about you. I was warned, but I did not at first recognize you!

CELESTINA. (Troy was a strong city, and others as savage have I tamed! No storm lasts for ever!)

MELIBEA. What are you saying, false woman? Speak up so that I can hear you! Can you justify yourself and appease my anger? Can you excuse your error and audacity?

CELESTINA. While you are angry you will not listen to me, for you are harsh and pitiless. But it is not surprising! Young blood is soon hot, with little cause.

MELIBEA. Little cause? It may well be cause enough for you to lose your life! Must I complain again of your audacity? What can I do for such a man as Calisto that will not sully my honour? Speak, since you say you have not finished, and see if you can atone for the past!

CELESTINA. Lady, I came for nothing but a prayer to St Apollonia, good against the toothache! He was told that you knew it. The only other thing I would ask of you is your girdle, which, as is well known, has touched the holy relics of Rome and Jerusalem. The young gentleman of whom I spoke suffers cruelly from the toothache. That's all I came for!

But since I have made you so angry, let him bear the pain as a punishment for having chosen so bad a messenger. But I would as soon have expected the rivers to run dry as you to fail in generosity of spirit! Yet you know well that vengeance is the pleasure of a moment, while pity lasts eternally.

MELIBEA. If that was all you wanted why didn't you say so at once? Why wrap it up in so many flowery speeches?

CELESTINA. My intentions were honourable! I did not think anyone would think evil of me if I mentioned them. If I erred in my approach to you, it was only because truth does not need to be dressed up. Pity for his pain, confidence in your clemency, caused me to express myself badly, and, as you know, madam, grief hangs heavy on the tongue and makes us say things we do not mean. Before God, you cannot blame me! If the young gentleman did wrong it is not my fault. I am only the messenger of the culprit. Do not attack the weakest link in the chain; do not, like the spider, which only preys on weaker insects, make the just suffer for the unjust. Imitate divine justice, which says: 'The soul that sinned must perish utterly.' Even Roman law does not condemn the father for the son's crime, nor the son for the father's! It is not right, lady, that I should be punished for Calisto's faults. Though, to speak the truth, he is no more deserving of punishment than I am, poor young man! I only wanted to help my neighbour. That is all I live for, it is my only consolation. I have never angered one man to please another, though they may have spoken evil of me behind my back. But the breath of calumny cannot prevail against the truth. My conscience is quite clear in this business. There are very few people in this city who are not beholden to me. They have only to ask, and I run to do what I can, as if I had twenty hands and as many feet!

MELIBEA. I no longer marvel that they say 'evil communications corrupt good manners!' I have heard so much of your wicked schemes that even now I do not know whether to believe you! Did you really come only for a prayer?

CELESTINA. May I never utter a prayer again, and may it never be answered, if I came for any other reason!

MELIBEA. I am so angry still that I cannot even laugh at you as you deserve! I know torments and oaths will not make you speak the truth, for you never have!

CELESTINA. You are the mistress here—I must hold my tongue and do as you wish. I am yours to command. Your cruellest word will seem to me a gentle benediction.

MELIBEA. You have well deserved my censure.

CELESTINA. I may have deserved it by what I said, but not by what I intended to say.

MELIBEA. You defend yourself so well that I shall finish by believing you! I will suspend judgment for the moment and give you the benefit of the doubt. I will not condemn you, for I may have made a mistake. But you must not be surprised at my anger, for you combined two things in your request, either of which alone would have driven me into a fury. First you mentioned the man who had had the audacity to accost me, and then you asked me for a message for him, but gave no reason for it. So I could only suppose he intended an attempt on my honour. But since you had a good reason for coming here I will forgive you. I am glad to know that my help is sought for a pious and holy action—for such it is to help the sick and afflicted!

CELESTINA. And so afflicted, good lady! Before God, if you knew him better you would not judge him as harshly as you do now! On my soul, he has no wickedness in him, but is compounded of a thousand virtues! Generous as Alexander, brave as Hector, majestic as a king, gracious, gay, in no way given to melancholy, of noble birth, as you know, a fine horseman, in feats of arms a St George, in force and courage a Hercules! His presence, his demeanour, his character, his elegance, cannot be described in words! He is altogether an angel from heaven! On my life, I think Narcissus, who fell in love with his own face when he saw it reflected in the water, was not more beautiful than this young gentleman! But alas, lady, he suffers cruelly from an aching tooth, of which he complains without ceasing.

MELIBEA. How long has he——

CELESTINA. He would be about three-and-twenty, not more. I was there when he was born, and took him from his mother's womb.

MELIBEA. I did not ask you that! I have no desire to know how old he is! I only wanted to know how long he has been suffering from the toothache.

CELESTINA. Lady, about a week. But you might think it a year, he is so altered. The only remedy he has is to take up his lute and sing such lamentable songs that I think they were written by the emperor Hadrian, that great lover of music. They are all about the departure of the soul and courage in the face of death. Though I know nothing about music, it seems to me that he makes his lute speak! When he sings the birds take greater pleasure in listening to him than if he were that famous singer of antiquity who, it is said, moved stones and trees by his music. If Calisto had been alive then they would not have made so great a case of Orpheus! Think, madam, what joy it would give me to restore health and strength to one who combines such qualities! Every woman who sees him praises God for having created him! If he speaks to her she is no longer mistress of herself, but his to command! After all this, madam, judge if my intention was good, my errand reasonable and above suspicion!

MELIBEA. Oh, I blame myself for my impatience! Because I did not realize your good intentions you had to suffer the lash of my sharp tongue! But I find it in my heart to forgive myself, for it was your long speeches which made me suspicious.

In recompense of your sufferings I will grant your request and give you my girdle. I shall not have time to write out the prayer before my mother comes home. But if the girdle does not cure him come back here to-morrow secretly.

LUCRETIA. Oh, my mistress is lost! She wants Celestina to come to her secretly! She dissembles, she promises her a prayer; but she means to give her more than that!

MELIBEA. What are you saying, Lucretia?

LUCRETIA. Lady, you have talked long enough—it grows late.

MELIBEA. Hear me, good mother, do not tell the young gentleman what has happened, or he will think me cruel, bad-tempered, and shrewish.

LUCRETIA. I was right! Things are going badly!

CELESTINA. I marvel much, lady Melibea, that you should doubt my discretion! Fear not, I can suffer in silence! But I see you are still suspicious and put little trust in me. I am glad that I can at least return to him with your girdle. I am sure his heart has already told him of your goodness to us and I shall find him much improved.

MELIBEA. I will do more for your patient, if necessary, and so make amends for my unkindness to you.

CELESTINA. (More will be necessary, you will do it, and we shall not even bother to thank you!)

MELIBEA. What are you saying, mother, about thanking me?

CELESTINA. I am saying, lady, that we shall all thank you, and serve you, and be much obliged to you. For when we know payment is expected the more ready we are to pay it.

LUCRETIA. Now, explain that, if you can!

CELESTINA. Ah, Lucretia, my dear child, come and see me some time, and I will give you a lotion which will make your hair as bright as gold. Don't tell your mistress! And I will give you a powder which will cure your bad breath. I am the only woman in the kingdom who knows how to make it! For nothing is more displeasing in a woman than foul breath.

LUCRETIA.　Oh, God bless you, old woman!　I need that more than a good meal!

CELESTINA.　Then why do you mutter against me, you silly wench?　You keep quiet, for you never know when you may need my help for something really serious!　Don't make your mistress more angry than she is already!　And now let me go in peace.

MELIBEA.　What are you saying to her, mother?

CELESTINA.　Oh, just a little joke!

MELIBEA.　Tell me!　I don't like people whispering in my presence and saying things I can't hear!

CELESTINA.　Lady, I asked her to remind you about the prayer. I said perhaps she would write it out for you.　And I told her to learn from me how to support your anger, for they say: 'Leave an angry man for a moment, an enemy for ever!' You, madam, were angry with me for what I said, but you are not my enemy.　And even if I had meant what you suspected, where was the harm in it?　Every day men suffer because of women, women because of men.　Nature wills it so, and nature was created by God, Who never does ill.　Therefore, whatever my request, it was praiseworthy, since it came from such a source, and I have nothing to reproach myself with.　I could give you many reasons in support of my argument, but too much talking wearies the hearer and may do harm to the speaker.

MELIBEA.　You have behaved very well throughout, as much in keeping silence when I was angry as in bearing my anger patiently.

CELESTINA.　Lady, I suffered in silence because you had some reason to be angry.　Anger is like lightning; it strikes quickly but does not last long.　So I bore your cruel words until you had exhausted your stock of them.

MELIBEA.　The young man should be grateful to you!

CELESTINA.　Lady, he deserves all I can do for him!　I am glad that my prayers have obtained some relief for his pain; but while I linger here he lies in misery.   I will go to him straight away, if you will permit me?

MELIBEA.   If you had asked me for my girdle immediately I would have given it without hesitation. Go with God! Your message brought me no profit; your departure can do me no harm.

ACT FIVE

SUMMARY: *Leaving Melibea, Celestina goes home, muttering under her breath. She finds Sempronio waiting for her. Deep in conversation, they go together to Calisto's house, and are seen by Parmeno, who warns his master of their approach. Celestina calls to Parmeno to open the door to them.*

CELESTINA. Oh, what a terrible moment! But what wise audacity! What superhuman patience! I should have been in danger of death if my wisdom had not made me prudent in my demands. How the virtuous young woman threatened me! Oh, what an angry young lady! O Devil that I conjured up, how well you kept your promise and did all I asked! I am indeed grateful to you! How cleverly you tamed the young lady and spirited away the mother so that I had time to coax her! Well done, old Celestina! Aren't you proud of yourself? Well begun is half done! O wonderful serpent's oil, marvellous white cord! How you turned all in my favour! If I had failed I should have renounced my witch-craft, and put no more faith in simples, stones, or words. You do well to rejoice, old woman! You will gain more by this than by refashioning fifteen virginities! Oh, how my wretched skirts hamper me and stop me from hastening to where I long to tell my good news! Fortune, how you favour the bold and desert the cowardly! The wretch who runs away cannot escape death. How many women would have failed in the task I set myself! What would they have done in such a situation, those youngsters who think to rival me? They would have answered back angrily and so lost all that

I, by my silence, have gained. No wonder they say: 'The cobbler should stick to his last!' Experience is a better teacher than books. Practice makes perfect, and it's made this old woman, who has enough sense to keep her petticoats out of the mud, a past mistress of her art. O blessed belt! If I live I will see you given back to her who was so unwilling to part with you!

SEMPRONIO. If I am not mistaken, here comes Celestina! Why, what the devil? How she swishes her skirts as she trots along! What is she muttering about under her breath?

CELESTINA. Why do you look so surprised, Sempronio? Didn't you expect to see me?

SEMPRONIO. Surprised? I'll tell you. Anything unusual excites our interest, and that interest, entering through the eyes, affects the mind, and the mind shows its effects by outward signs. Now, whoever saw you as you were just now, walking along, with your head down and your eyes on the ground, taking no notice of anything? Whoever heard you muttering under your breath as you came along, and running as if you were on to a good thing? By my faith, that is unusual enough to make anyone marvel! But enough of that! For God's sake tell me the news! What has He sent us? I've been waiting here over an hour, but I said to myself: 'No news is good news!'

CELESTINA. My son, that foolish saying is not always true! You might have waited longer and had bad news in the end. For I nearly lost the tip of my nose, and my tongue too!

SEMPRONIO. For God's sake, mother, don't keep me in suspense! Tell me everything that happened!

CELESTINA. This is neither the time nor the place. Come with me to Calisto, and you shall hear great tidings. I shall only spoil it by telling you now. I want Calisto to hear from my own mouth what has happened, for though you may take a small part of the profit, remember, I did all the work!

SEMPRONIO. A small part indeed! Come, Celestina, that's no way to talk!

CELESTINA. Be quiet, hothead! Small or large, you shall have all you want. What's mine is thine! Let us enjoy it and profit by it, and not quarrel over the distribution! All the same, old people need more than young, and I certainly need more than you, for you are sure of a roof over your head and three good meals a day.

SEMPRONIO. I need something besides food.

CELESTINA. What, my son? A dozen shoulder-knots? A jewelled buckle for your hat? A bow and arrow so that you can go shooting sparrows, and ogling the little birds in the windows, the young birds that can't fly—you understand me? There is no better pander than your bow! It gives you the entry everywhere after a lost arrow! But oh, Sempronio, how hard it is for an old woman to live honestly!

SEMPRONIO. (Oh, the treacherous old hag, the wicked witch! The greedy, avaricious creature! She hopes to profit by deceiving me, as she deceives my master! But she'll gain nothing by it. I don't envy her her riches. He who rises by dishonest means will fall faster than he rose. How difficult it is to judge one's fellow men! Well may they say there are no animals or merchandise so difficult to assess! The old woman is false and evil. The devil drove me to her. I should have done better to keep away from the venomous viper! It is all my own fault. But whatever happens, I'll see she keeps her promises.)

CELESTINA. What are you saying, Sempronio? Who are you talking to? You are getting all tangled up in my skirts. Why don't you walk faster?

SEMPRONIO. I was saying, good mother, that I ought not to be surprised if you change your mind, for all women are the same. It seems to me, however, that you are going the wrong way to work in this matter. Here you are, rushing off to

Calisto with good news, when you know how much more precious a thing is when one has had to wait for it. The longer he is left in uncertainty the greater our profit.

CELESTINA. The wise man knows when to bide his time. Only a fool is obstinate. A changing situation must be met with new ideas. I did not think, son Sempronio, that my luck would be so good. A discreet messenger knows how to profit by a good opportunity. One can never make up for lost time. I know by experience that your master is generous, but capricious. He will give more in one day for good news than in a month of uncertainty, while I wear myself out with comings and goings. The swift and unexpected news I bring will throw him into confusion, and that will prevent him thinking clearly. Besides, what can come of good news but something good? And what of a noble nature but costly gifts? Go to, boy, you may trust the old woman in this matter!

SEMPRONIO. What passed between you and the young lady? Tell me what she said! Before God, I am almost as anxious for good news as my master!

CELESTINA. Be quiet, idiot, it has nothing to do with you. I see you would rather have the profit of this business than the worry of it! Let us hurry or your master will run mad while we delay.

SEMPRONIO. He's mad already!

PARMENO. Sir, sir!

CALISTO. Well, fool?

PARMENO. I see Sempronio and Celestina coming. They keep stopping, and Sempronio is drawing lines in the dust with the point of his sword. I cannot think what they are doing!

CALISTO. O negligent and unhelpful slave! If you see them coming why don't you run and open the door? O God, sovereign deity! What does this visit portend? What news do they bring me? They have delayed so long that I look forward to their arrival almost more than to the end of my sufferings.   O ears, prepare yourselves, for my fate now lies in the mouth of Celestina!   Could I but sleep away the time between the beginning and the end of her speech!   Now I know that the condemned man awaits his death sentence with more apprehension than his final execution!   O blundering Parmeno, is there no strength in your puny hands?   Open the door and let in the good old woman who holds my life in her hands.

CELESTINA   You hear that, Sempronio?   Your master has changed his tune!   That's rather different from what we heard him say to Parmeno when we first came!   Things are getting better and better.   Every word he speaks is worth at least a new silk petticoat for Celestina!

SEMPRONIO.   When you go in pretend not to see Calisto and say something flattering about him.

CELESTINA.   Be quiet, Sempronio!   Though I have risked my life for Calisto, yet he deserves an answer to his prayers—and thine—and I hope to receive a fitting reward!

ACT SIX

SUMMARY: *Celestina, going into Calisto's house, is eagerly entreated to relate what has passed between her and Melibea. While Celestina and Calisto are talking, Parmeno makes sarcastic remarks to Sempronio, who tries to stop him. Finally Celestina gives Calisto Melibea's girdle and takes her leave, returning to her own home with Parmeno.*

CALISTO. What news, good mother, what news?

CELESTINA. O my good lord Calisto, are you there? O happy lover of the most beautiful Melibea! How will you reward the poor old woman who has to-day risked her life in your service? What woman was ever in such a perilous position as I? Even to think of it makes my blood run cold! I wouldn't have given as much for my life as would suffice to buy this ragged old cloak of mine!

PARMENO. Always on about yourself! Always pushing your petty concerns into our important business! That's only the first step! Soon you'll be wanting a silk dress! Always something for yourself, never anything that can be shared! You want to feather your own nest, you old bawd! You will force me to speak out and make my master angry if you go on like this. Listen carefully, Sempronio! You'll see, she won't ask for money, because that's too easily shared!

SEMPRONIO. Hold your peace, fool! If Calisto hears you he will kill you!

CALISTO. Mother, for God's sake cut short your explanations, or take my sword and kill me!

66

PARMENO. The poor devil shakes as if with ague! He can hardly stand up. He would give the old hag his tongue if it would make her speak more quickly. He won't last long! We shall soon wear mourning for him!

CELESTINA. Your sword, sir? Why, what mean you? Keep your sword for your enemies and for those that seek to harm you. I bring you comfort and good news from the one you love best.

CALISTO. Good news, lady?

CELESTINA. You can call it good, for the door stands open for my return, and I shall be better received, in my poor old rags, than many a one in silks and brocade.

PARMENO. Sew up my mouth, Sempronio, or I shall say something I shall regret! I told you we should soon come to the silk dress!

SEMPRONIO. Be quiet, will you, or I'll send you to the devil! What does it matter if she does draw attention to her rags? She certainly needs new clothes, and, as they say: 'The labourer is worthy of his hire!'

PARMENO. At least he works for what he gets! But this old bawd wants more for five minutes' cozenage than a man could earn by honest labour in fifty years!

SEMPRONIO. Is that all the gratitude you show to the old woman who brought you up? Is that what you learnt in her service?

PARMENO. I don't mind how much she asks for as long as we get our share.

SEMPRONIO. Her greatest sin is avarice. But while she feathers her own nest she mustn't forget to feather ours too, or I'll know the reason why!

CALISTO. Tell me, mother, for God's sake, what happened? How did you get into the house? Which room did you go into? How did she receive you?

CELESTINA. She received me, sir, as savage bulls receive those who stick darts into them in the bull-ring, or as wild boars receive the hunters who hold them at bay!

CALISTO. Do you call that good news? Then what would your bad news be? It could not be death, for that would end the torments which now afflict me.

SEMPRONIO. My master cries out before he is hurt! What a fool he is! Can't he wait patiently to hear what he has so ardently longed for?

PARMENO. Now it's your turn to hold your tongue, Sempronio! If our master hears you he will punish you as well as me!

SEMPRONIO. Oh, go to hell! You haven't a good word for anybody! What have I said to offend you? The pox take you, you damned envious quarrelsome lackey! Is this the friendship you promised Celestina to show me? Be off with you!

CALISTO. Good old woman, if you do not want to plunge me into despair, and condemn me to perpetual torment, leave this trifling! Tell me plainly if your petition was not well received, and if she, divine author of my death, showed herself always so cruel and unyielding? For what you have told me so far gives more proof of hate than of love.

CELESTINA. The great virtue of the honey-bee—in which she should be imitated by all wise men—is that she turns all she touches to her profit. As I did with the cruel and disdainful words of your Melibea! Her severity I turned to honey, her anger to pity, her fury to calm. Why, what else did you expect of this poor old Celestina whom you have so generously rewarded above her deserts? I calmed your beloved's anger, suffered her scorn, shielded you in your absence, received on my back the blows, the insults, the contempt, and the disdain with which all young women receive the first avowal of love, in order to make their later capitulation more precious! Those they most desire they speak to most harshly! Why, there would be no difference between the common slut and the fine lady if both answered 'Yes!' to the first demand of love! Young ladies, however much they kindle and burn with the cruel fires of love, must for their honour's sake preserve a calm demeanour, a countenance unmoved, a serene indifference, a firm spirit, a chaste purpose, and a bitter tongue, so that their own mouths marvel at their dissimulation, which forces them to say the opposite of what they feel! And now, so that you may calm yourself and remain silent while I tell you in full the progress of my errand, and the excuse I found to approach your lady, know that the end of the affair was very satisfactory!

CALISTO. Lady, now that you have given me that assurance I can bear all the rigours of her replies. Say what you will, and how you will, I will listen quietly. My heart is at peace, my apprehensions are calmed, the blood flows again in my veins. I have lost all my fears, I am happy! Let us go up to my room! There, if you wish, you can tell me in full what you have only hinted at here below.

CELESTINA. Let us go up, sir!

PARMENO. Oh, holy Virgin, how ready this madman is to leave us in order to weep out his joy with Celestina, and unveil to her all the secrets of his incontinent and lascivious appetites! Now will he ask and hear six times the same thing, without anyone to reproach him for his prolixity! But be easy, sir, we'll be there with you!

CALISTO. Look, lady, how happy Parmeno is! See how he crosses himself for joy that you have served me so diligently! On my life, he must have been worried about you, for see, he crosses himself again! Now, come up, come up, mother, and sit yourself down! And I will sit here at your feet to hear your happy news. Tell me first, how did you get into the house?

CELESTINA. I was selling some yarn—I've caught many a one that way, God be praised for it, and some greater than she!

CALISTO. In worldly estimation, perhaps, but no greater in elegance, in wit, in grace and virtue, discretion, estate and birth, or in sweetness of speech.

PARMENO. How he runs on with his foolish chatter! He's like a clock that never strikes less than twelve at noon! You listen to them, Sempronio, for I am quite deafened by it all, what with his foolishness and her untruthfulness.

SEMPRONIO. You venomous viper! Why should you wish to shut your ears to that which all the world wants to hear, like a snake deaf to the voice of the snake-charmer? They speak of love, and even if they lie you should hear them with care and attention.

CELESTINA. Listen, lord Calisto, and you will hear the result of my vigilance and your good luck! While we were bargaining over my yarn, Melibea's mother was called away to visit her sick sister, and as she had to go at once she left Melibea to finish the business with me.

CALISTO. O joy beyond compare! O rare opportunity! O fortunate chance! Could I but have been hidden under your cloak, to hear her speak in whom God has joined so many graces!

CELESTINA. Under my cloak, say you? Why, God save you, sir, you would soon have been discovered through its many holes, may God mend it!

PARMENO. I'm off, Sempronio! I'll hear no more. You can listen if you like. If my master wasn't bemused with counting the steps between here and Melibea's house, with wondering over her beauty, and imagining how she looked while she haggled over the old woman's thread, and what thoughts then occupied her mind, he would realize that my advice was more salutary to him than all the lies of Celestina!

CALISTO. Where are you going, Parmeno? I am listening with all my attention to her who brings me life, and there you are, chattering, fidgeting, doing all you can to irritate and annoy me! For God's sake be quiet! You should take pleasure in hearing the old woman's account of her work. Tell me, mother, what did you do when you found yourself alone with her?

CELESTINA.   I was so overcome with joy that I am sure anyone would have guessed it from the look on my face!

CALISTO.   That is how I feel at this moment! What must it have been like for you, face to face with her beauty! No doubt you were struck dumb with admiration?

CELESTINA.   On the contrary! Being alone with her gave me courage to say what I had in mind. I spoke frankly. I told her my errand, I told her you were sick and near to death, and begged for one word from her mouth which would cure your disease. And while she stared at me in surprise, taken aback by so unexpected a message, wondering who it could be that suffered so, and how a word from her could effect a cure, I spoke your name! She stopped me, and put her hand to her head like one who hears bad news. She ordered me to be quiet and to go away, unless I wished her servants to put me to death. She upbraided me for my audacity, called me a witch, a whore, a traitress, a hag, an evildoer, and many other ugly names with which we frighten children in their cradles! Then she swooned away, fell into convulsions, lost her senses, tossed herself from side to side, tormented by the golden arrow that transfixed her when I spoke your name. Her body twisted, her hands clasped as if in despair, she seemed ready to tear herself in pieces! She cast furious glances on all sides, tapped her foot violently on the hard ground. And I, all this while, huddled in a corner, squatted on the ground, and never said a word! The more she raged the better pleased I was, for I saw the moment approaching when she would have to give in. And while she worked herself up into a passion, I did not indulge in vain or foolish fears, but calmly took advantage of the time to decide what I should say next.

CALISTO. I too was wondering about that while you were speaking, and could not think of any excuse which would explain away what you had said, without making her suspect the true end of your demand. But I know how wise you are! Truly, you seem to me greater than mortal woman, and since you were able to foresee her first reaction to your words, no doubt you were also able to prepare your defence? No greater power had the Tuscan Adeleta (whose fame, had you lived then, would have been less!) who three days before she died foretold the manner of death of her old husband and her two sons. I now believe what they say, that weak women are more cunning than the strongest men!

CELESTINA. Well, sir, I told her you were suffering from terrible toothache, and that the only word I wanted from her was a prayer she was reputed to know, most efficacious against that torment!

CALISTO. O wonderful guile! O woman unique in your kind! O cautious creature, quick-witted sorceress! O discreet messenger! Who else would have thought of so ingenious an excuse? I am sure that if Dido and Aeneas were alive now, Venus would have no difficulty in making them fall in love! There would have been no need for Cupid to disguise himself as Ascanius! You would have been the only go-between! Now I resign the whole affair into your hands, for even if I do not achieve my ends I shall know that you have done all that is humanly possible on my behalf. What do you say to that, lads? What could have been better thought of? Is there a wiser woman alive in this world to-day?

CELESTINA. Sir, don't interrupt me! Let me finish, for night is coming on. You know wicked men shun the daylight, and returning home in the dark I may meet with some ruffians!

CALISTO. No, no! There are torches here to light you home, and pages enough to carry them!

PARMENO. Poor little innocent, she's afraid of being raped!

You had better go with her, Sempronio, in case she meets a bogyman in the dark!

CALISTO. What say you, friend Parmeno?

PARMENO. Sir, that Sempronio and I had better see her home, as the night is very dark.

CALISTO. Well said! That is a very good idea! Now, continue your story, good mother, and tell me what happened next? What said Melibea to your request for the prayer?

CELESTINA. That she would willingly grant it.

CALISTO. Willingly? O gift beyond all price!

CELESTINA. But I asked for something more.

CALISTO. What was that, O honourable old woman?

CELESTINA. A girdle that she wears constantly. I told her it would allay your sufferings, for it has touched many saintly relics.

CALISTO. What did she say to that?

CELESTINA. Give me my reward and I will tell you!

CALISTO. Oh, take my house and all that is in it! Tell me what you want and it is yours!

CELESTINA. I want nothing but a cloak to keep this poor old body warm, and in return I'll give you Melibea's girdle!

CALISTO. A cloak only? No, a cloak, a dress, and whatever else you require!

CELESTINA. I only want a cloak, and that will be enough. Say no more, and don't offer me anything else, for they say that to offer more to one who asks only a little is in its way a kind of refusal.

CALISTO. Parmeno, run, call my tailor, tell him to cut a cloak and dress for Celestina from that cloth I sent him.

PARMENO. I knew how it would be! Presents for the old woman, who comes here laden like a bee with lies, and nothing for me, though I do all their errands! She thinks of no one but herself in all her comings and goings!

CALISTO. What's the matter with the sulky fellow? There is

no man worse served than I! My servants are always grumbling, unwilling, muttering, and scowling! What, are you envious, you good-for-nothing? What are you muttering that I can't hear? Do as I tell you and don't make me angry! I have enough to put up with as it is! Run along! There may be enough stuff left over for a doublet for you if you hurry.

PARMENO. Sir, all I said was that it is rather late to fetch the tailor.

CALISTO. I knew you would have some objection! Then tell him to come to-morrow. And you, lady, be patient, for my sake! You won't lose by this delay. But now let me see this blessed girdle, worthy of binding so slender a waist! Rejoice, my eyes and all my other senses, which have so long suffered together! Be happy, poor heart, which has not known one moment's peace since first I saw that lovely lady! All my senses were wounded, each grieved worse than the other. Eyes from seeing her, ears from hearing her, hands from touching her——

CELESTINA. When have you touched her, pray? The mere thought of it terrifies me!

CALISTO. In dreams, I mean.

CELESTINA. Dreams?

CALISTO. Every night I see her in my dreams. I fear to become like Alcibiades, who dreamed that he was wrapped in his mistress's mantle, and when he was murdered no one would take up his body in the street, or even hide it from men's sight, until she covered it with her cloak! Yet, dead or alive, how much I would rejoice to wear what she has worn!

CELESTINA. Oh, you torment yourself too much! While others rest quietly in their beds, you go looking for fresh causes of pain and anguish. Be of good cheer, sir, God will not desert you! To calm your apprehensions take this girdle, and if I live you shall have also its mistress!

CALISTO. O happy gift! O blessed girdle, which has had the

honour to encircle that body that I am not worthy to touch! Girdle that I adore, you have embraced the object of all my desires! Tell me, did you hear the cruel words of her whom you served and I adore, for whom I languish night and day, and yet seem no nearer my desired end?

CELESTINA. It is an old saying that he who asks little may get much! I will obtain more for you by my prayers than you by your despair! Console yourself, sir. Zamora was not taken in an hour, and yet the attackers were not discouraged.

CALISTO. Oh, unhappy that I am! Cities have stone walls and battering-rams may break them down! But my mistress has a heart of steel. No metal can vanquish it, no arrow transfix it. If you put a ladder against the wall her eyes shoot arrows and her tongue reproachful words. She is so strongly fortified that one cannot get within half a mile of her!

CELESTINA. Softly, sir! Remember, one man's cunning caused the fall of Troy! And never doubt but that one woman will yield to another! You have not been in my house very often—you do not know what I can do!

CALISTO. Whatever you say in future, lady, I will believe it, since you have brought me this girdle to be my precious plaything. O glorious girdle of so heavenly a creature, I can hardly believe I hold you in my hand. Good girdle, were you my enemy? Tell me truly. If so I pardon you, for men should forgive their enemies. But I do not believe it! If you had been my enemy you would not have yielded so readily to my hand. Unless perhaps it were to excuse yourself? I charge you, by the power your mistress has over me, answer truly!

CELESTINA. Enough of such extravagances, young master! The girdle is all creased with your kisses.

CALISTO. O unhappy Calisto! Would to God, good girdle, that you were woven of my arms! With what joy and reverence would I clip and fondle that body which you, not knowing your good fortune, have so often held in your embraces! Oh, what secrets you have seen!

CELESTINA. You will see as much, and more, if you do not waste your time in such talk!

CALISTO. Quiet, lady, we understand each other! O my eyes, the first cause of my sorrow, the door by which the poison reached my heart, it is only right that consolation should come to me through you. You owe me my cure. And this is the only remedy that has so far come your way.

SEMPRONIO. Sir, you are so delighted with the girdle that you no longer think of Melibea!

CALISTO. What a fool, what a lunatic, what a kill-joy is this creature! What do you mean?

SEMPRONIO. That you tire yourself with these ravings and weary all those who hear you. And so you will lose your reason and your life. The least thing causes you to waste your strength in speech. Cease your babblings and listen to Celestina!

CALISTO. Do I weary you, mother, with my talk, or is this fool drunk?

CELESTINA. Even if he is, sir, you would do well to take his advice! Cease to lament and treat the girdle as it deserves! You cannot talk to it as to a person. Reserve your rhapsodies for Melibea!

CALISTO. O kind mother, dearest comforter! Let me enjoy the good augury of my future happiness! Why waste yourself, my tongue, on other subjects, why cease to hymn the priceless gift of her whom I may never possess! How carelessly and disrespectfully my hands handle the remedy of my deep wound! I need no longer fear the poisoned darts of love. Now I am safe, for she who wounded me supplies the remedy. And, good mother, joy of the old, delight of the young, comforter of such desolate lovers as I, do not trouble me with your complaints, for I suffer enough from my own woes! Let me rejoice freely, let me walk the streets with this jewel in my hands, so that all who see me may know that there is no happier man than I on earth!

SEMPRONIO. Do not aggravate your wound with such imaginings, sir! For it is not on the girdle alone that your cure must depend.

CALISTO. Too well I know it! But I cannot tear myself away from contemplation of this gift.

CELESTINA. Gift? No, that word is used for presents given willingly! This was given you for love of God, to cure your toothache; not for love of you, to cure your heartache! But never fear, if I live, it will come to that yet!

CALISTO. And what about the prayer?

CELESTINA. She did not give me that!

CALISTO. Why not?

CELESTINA. There was no time. But she said that if the pain did not abate I was to go back for it to-morrow.

CALISTO. Abate? My pain will abate only when she ceases to be cruel!

CELESTINA. Enough of that, sir! She is willing enough, it seems to me, to do all she can to cure your toothache. That must suffice for a first visit! Now I am off home! Take care, sir, if you go out to-morrow morning to muffle your face in a scarf, so that if she sees you she will not think I have told her a lie.

CALISTO. I will do whatever you say. But tell me, for the love of God, is that all that happened? I long to hear of further speech from those divine lips! How did you dare approach her, without knowing her, and show so much familiarity in your demand?

CELESTINA. Without knowing her? Why, we were neighbours for four years! I saw them every day, talked and laughed with them. Her mother knew me as I know myself.

And I must say Melibea has since become a charming and intelligent young woman!

PARMENO. Ha, listen, Sempronio!

SEMPRONIO. What is it?

PARMENO. This great deed of Celestina's has made our master more of a chatterbox than ever! Go nearer, tread on her toes, remind her that it is time we were off! However mad a man is, he doesn't talk quite so much when he is alone!

CALISTO. Charming and intelligent? Oh, you are joking! There was never such another woman born on earth! Did God ever create a more beautiful body? Could you paint so lovely a face, the perfection of all beauty? If Helen of Troy, for whom so many Greeks and Trojans died, were living now, or the lovely Polyxena, they would yield the palm to the queen of my heart! If she had been present with the three goddesses when Paris brought the apple, it would never have been called the apple of discord, for without hesitation all would have agreed to give it to Melibea. How many women, seeing her, rail on God because he did not endow them with her beauty? They consume away, eaten up with envy, and subject themselves to a severe martyrdom, thinking to equal artificially the perfection which she has by nature. Some pluck their eyebrows with tweezers, or with wax and creams; some collect yellow herbs, roots, branches and flowers, and concoct washes to make their hair as golden as hers; others slap their faces, or cover them with ointments and greases, strong lotions, red and white paint, and other things which I will not bother to enumerate! See then if Melibea, who has all this by nature, deserves for servant so poor a thing as I?

CELESTINA. All right, Sempronio! I know what you want! Wait a minute while he rides his hobby-horse! He'll soon tire the poor beast and fall off!

CALISTO. Nature has been pleased to make her perfect. All great gifts divided among other women are united in her, so

that whoever sees her must realize the greatness of her Creator.
With nothing more than a little cold water and an ivory comb
she can surpass in beauty all living women.   They are her only
weapons.   With these she has led me captive, with these she
holds me now in bondage and in heavy chains!

CELESTINA. Peace, peace, do not fret yourself! The bird-
lime I have is stronger than the charm that binds you. I will
cut your bonds and set you free! Meanwhile let me go, for
it is late, and give me back that girdle. I shall have need of it.

CALISTO. O wretch that I am! Misfortune dogs my steps!
With you, or with this girdle, or with both, I meant to spend
this long dark night. But there is no certain happiness in this
miserable life! Come, solitude, and keep me company! Ho
there!

PARMENO. Sir?

CALISTO. Accompany this lady to her house, and may as
much joy and happiness go with her as sadness and solitude
stay with me!

CELESTINA. God be with you, sir! To-morrow you will see
me again. I will bring you her answer and fetch my cloak,
since there was no time for that to-day. Meanwhile be
patient and think of other things!

CALISTO. That is impossible! It would be treachery to think
of anyone but her for whose sake alone I take pleasure in
being alive!

ACT SEVEN

SUMMARY: *Celestina talks to Parmeno, and tries to get him to agree to be friends with Sempronio. Parmeno reminds her of her promise to give him Areusa, whom he loves. They go to Areusa's house and Parmeno spends the night there. Celestina goes home and knocks at the door. Elicia opens it and reproaches her for returning so late.*

CELESTINA. Parmeno, my son, I have been so busy that I have not yet had an opportunity to prove myself your friend. But while you have been gone I have said all I could in your favour. There is no need to ask why, for I look on you as my son by adoption. And I thought you would treat me as a son should. But you have repaid my affection by miscalling me in front of Calisto, by criticizing all my remarks, and by murmuring and grumbling at me. I had hoped you would listen to my good advice and not turn against me. I am afraid you are still full of youthful vanity, and you often talk foolishly, less for your profit than to please your tongue. Listen to me now, as you do not seem to have listened before, and remember that I am old and therefore wise. For wisdom is the prerogative of old age, as pleasure is of youth. And truly I believe youth alone is the cause of all your faults. I hope to God that you behave better towards me in future, and that as you grow older you will become more sensible, for, as they say: 'Habits can change, like the colour of one's hair!' And as your hair goes grey, so you will see things differently! Youth lives only in the present, but old age looks to the past, present, and future. If you had remembered, son Parmeno, all I did for you in the past, the first house you would have visited on returning to this city would have been mine; but young men think little of old friends! You leave everything to chance, never considering that you may have need of us, never remembering our infirmities, or thinking that the bright flower of your youth will fade. But remember, friend, that in the hour of need an old woman can be a useful friend, a mother, and, more than a mother, a pleasant companion in health, a good nurse in sickness, a full purse when you are poor, a safe bank for your money when you are rich, a good fire in winter, when the meat roasts on the spit, a good shade in summer, a good inn at all times for food and drink. What say you to all this, little idiot? I hope you are ashamed of your behaviour this evening? That is all I ask. God Himself asks no more of the sinner than repentance and amendment of life. Look at Sempronio! God helping me, I made him a man. I want you two to be like brothers, for if you stand well with him you will also stand well with your master and with all the world. You see how he is welcomed everywhere. He is diligent, helpful, polite, and friendly. If he holds out the hand of friendship to you, you would do well to take it. No one stands nearer to your master than you two. And if you wish to have friends you must be friendly. You cannot tickle trout without getting your hands wet! Sempronio owes you nothing! It is foolish of you to repulse a friend and yet expect friendship, to repay liking with dislike.

PARMENO. Mother, I confess I was in the wrong. Forgive me and advise me what to do for the best in future. I fear that friendship with Sempronio is not possible. He is quick-tempered and I am easily roused. How can we be friends?

CELESTINA. But you used not to be like that!

PARMENO. On my life, the longer I live the more irritable I become! I am not what I was. Besides, nothing about Sempronio attracts me.

CELESTINA. The true friend is known in moments of disaster, and proves his worth in adversity. He is a regular visitor to the house that good luck has deserted. How can I describe to you, my son, the virtues of true friendship? There is nothing more wonderful or more rare! A true friend never refuses to share your burdens. And you and Sempronio are so alike, the similarity of your tastes and desires should cement your friendship. And don't forget, my son, that I have something in reserve for you! It is in safe keeping, and when you earn some more, that can be added to it. Blessed be the good father who laid up this little fortune for you! I will give it to you when you are older and more settled in life.

PARMENO. Tell me, mother, what do you mean by settled?

CELESTINA. Strike out for yourself, my son, and don't be content to serve always in another's house, as you will do if you don't know how to profit by experience! It was out of pity for your shabbiness that I asked Calisto for a cloak. Not because I wanted one, but because once the tailor was in the house, and your master saw how much you needed a new doublet, he would order one for you. So it was not for my sake only that I spoke (as you seemed to think) but for yours also! If you wait to be offered presents by these gallants, you'll be able to count on the fingers of one hand all you'll get in ten years! Make the most of your youth; eat well, drink well, enjoy yourself night and day! Take all you can get, for opportunity never knocks twice! Do not scruple to make use of the wealth your master has inherited. Profit by it in this world, for it is of no use in the next! O son Parmeno (and well may I call you my son, seeing how long I have known you!), take my advice, which I proffer for no other reason than to see you succeed in life. What pleasure it would give me to see you and Sempronio better friends, good brothers, united in affection, visiting my poor house together to take your ease and enjoy my young girls!

PARMENO. Young girls, mother?

CELESTINA. Yes, truly, for I am too old to be of much use to you! I have got a good wench for Sempronio, and with less reason, for I am not as fond of him as I am of you.   I say this from the bottom of my heart!

PARMENO.   You shall see, good mother, I am not ungrateful.

CELESTINA.   Even if you were, it would not grieve me too much!   All I do is done for the love of God, and because I am sorry for you, alone in a hostile world.   And also out of respect for the memory of your mother, who confided you to me.   When you are a man you will understand better, and then you will say 'Old Celestina gave me good advice!'

PARMENO.   I say it already, though I am only a boy.   I spoke as I did to-day, not because I blamed you, but because I had already made my master angry by offering him good advice.   From now on let us all be against him.   Say what you like, I will be silent.   I was wrong not to trust you from the beginning.

CELESTINA.   And you will be wrong again if you do not follow my advice.   Believe me, it comes from a good friend!

PARMENO.   I am sure the time I spent in your service was well spent, since I can profit so much by it now.   And I pray to God for the soul of my father, who left me such a good friend, and of my mother, who placed me in such good hands.

CELESTINA.   Ah, don't speak of her, my dear, unless you wish to see me in tears!   Never again in this world shall I find such a friend, such a companion, such a comforter in all my trials and troubles!   She was more than a sister to me.   Who but your mother covered up my mistakes, knew my secrets, read into my inmost soul?   She was all my happiness and repose. How gay she was, how brisk, how lively and high-spirited! Off she would go, at midnight, as boldly as if it had been broad daylight, from one cemetery to another, collecting what we needed for our work!   There was no grave, of Christian, of Jew, or of Moor, that she left unvisited!   By day she marked them, by night she dug them up.   She enjoyed the dark night as you the clear light of day.   She said it covered a multitude

of sins! And she was shrewd too! Oh, she had all the virtues!
I'll tell you something she did that will make you realize what
a mother you had! It ought not to be told, but I trust you!
She drew seven teeth from a hanged man with a pair of eyebrow
tweezers while I was taking off his shoes! As for entering the
charmed circle, she did it better than I, and more bravely,
though I had a good reputation for fearlessness! But all
that is over now that she is gone. I tell you, the devils themselves feared her! They trembled and cowered under her
terrible incantations. She was as familiar with them all as
you with your own household. They came tumbling one
after the other when she called them. And they never dared
to lie to her, she had such power over them! Since she went
I have never known them speak one word of truth.

PARMENO. (God bless the old creature, how she amuses me
with her silly gossip!)

CELESTINA. What do you say, my dear Parmeno, my son and
more than son?

PARMENO. I said how was it that my mother had such power,
since you both used the same spells?

CELESTINA. Why should that surprise you? Don't you know
the old saying: 'Kissing goes by favour'? We can't all expect
to have her wonderful powers. You must have seen how some
men become pre-eminent in their profession, while others as
well gifted get nowhere? Your mother, God rest her soul,
was foremost among us all, known and recognized as past
mistress of her art by all the world: gentlefolk, clergy, young
men, old men, even children! As for the young girls, they
remembered her in their prayers side by side with their own
parents! She helped everyone, talked to anyone! If we
went out everyone we met in the street called her 'Godmother'
—for she was sixteen years a midwife! You were too young
to know all this before, but now that you are a man, and she
is dead, it is only right that you should be told.

PARMENO. Tell me, lady, when the police came to arrest you, while I was still in your service, were you friendly with her then?

CELESTINA. Friendly with her then? Why, you must be joking! We were in that affair together! We were seen, arrested, and charged together, and together received our punishment. And that was the first time we were caught! But I am surprised you remember it. You were very young then. It's all forgotten now. These things happen to the best of us. Every day you see people who sin and pay the penalty for sinning.

PARMENO. That is true. But surely the worst sin is to continue sinning? The first time it may be unavoidable, like a sudden, unintentional movement. Therefore they say: 'There is joy in heaven over one sinner that repenteth!'

CELESTINA. (Poor little idiot! I can't help feeling sorry for you! But what have we to do with repentance? Never mind, you'll soon learn!)

PARMENO. What say you, mother?

CELESTINA. I was just remembering, my son, that, not counting that occasion, your mother, God pity her, was arrested four times. Once for witchcraft, because she was found by night with a lantern taking earth from a suicide's grave at the cross-roads. She was kept all day on a scaffold raised in the city square, with the cap of infamy on her head. But that was nothing! We must all suffer in this sad world if we wish to live and thrive. You can see how unimportant it was, for she was never any the worse for it, nor did she alter her way of life. And that brings us to what you were saying about continuing in sin. She was superb in everything she did. On my life, she had such assurance and aplomb, exposed there on that scaffold, that she seemed to care nothing for the curious crowd thronging round her. It is always the bravest and wisest, like your mother, who have to pay most dearly for their mistakes.   Remember Virgil!   He was wise enough, and yet, as you know, he was hung from a tower in an osier basket, exposed to the view of all Rome.   But for all that he was not dishonoured, nor did he lose the name of Virgil.

PARMENO.   That is true, but it was not done by the hand of justice.

CELESTINA.   Quiet, child!   What do you know of canonical law?   By the hand of justice or any other hand—does it matter?   Our parish priest, God be good to him, knew that when he came to console with your mother.   He said, blessed were those who were persecuted for righteousness' sake, for they would inherit the kingdom of heaven; and that one must suffer in this world, to be sure of enjoying the next.   And though she had been wrongfully accused and arrested without proof, and had, by false witnesses and cruel tortures, been made to confess herself what she was not, yet she had such courage and a heart so strong in suffering that she could support ill usage and be none the worse for it.   I myself heard her say twenty times: 'What does it matter if they crushed my foot?   It was all to my advantage, for I am now better known than ever!'   When we remember all she suffered on earth, she must be enjoying her reward now in heaven—if what the priest said was true!   That's my only consolation. And now you must take her place by my side, and be my true friend.   Strive always to do what is right, and above all take care to seem virtuous, and you will soon merit the inheritance your father left you.

PARMENO.   Oh, enough of the dead and their leavings!   Let us talk of the present and not of the past.   Have you forgotten that not very long ago you promised me Areusa?   I told you when you were at our house that I was dying for love of her.

CELESTINA.   If I promised I will keep my promise.   You need not think I am so old as to have lost my memory!   I've made several approaches to her in your absence, and not without some success! I think the time is ripe for something more direct. Let us go to her house! I tell you, this is nothing compared with what I will do for you!

PARMENO. I have been in the depths of despair, for whenever I had a chance of being with her she was as silent as the grave. And they say a still tongue is a bad omen in love. So I had lost all hope.

CELESTINA. There is no need to despair now I am on your side. I will help you, and I know what I am doing in such matters! You'll see soon enough what a help I can be, how I handle such ticklish creatures, and manage their love affairs! Softly now, here we are at her door! Let us go in quietly so that the neighbours don't hear us! Wait here at the bottom of the stairs. I will go up and see how the land lies. And perhaps we shall accomplish more than we hope for!

AREUSA. Who is there? Who dares to come up into my bedroom at this time of night?

CELESTINA. Only a poor old woman who wishes you well; one who never stirs a step without thinking of your welfare, who worries more over you than over herself; one who loves you, though she may be old!

AREUSA. (The devil take the old hag, coming in like a ghost at this time of night!) Come in, old lady, what good fortune brings you here so late? I was just going to bed.

CELESTINA. Going to bed with the sun, my child? That's not the way to thrive! It would be better to walk abroad at such a time. You don't need to languish here alone, looking for crumbs on a bare board! Ah, you lead a fine life! Many a one would be glad of it!

AREUSA. Wait while I get dressed again. It's cold!

CELESTINA. No, don't do that, on my life, get into bed! Then we can talk.

AREUSA. Well, I shall be glad enough to get between the

sheets! I have been feeling ill all day. It was that, rather than laziness, that sent me to bed so early.

CELESTINA. Off with your clothes then, and into bed with you! What a little beauty you are! How sweet your dress smells as you fold it! Ah, nothing succeeds like success! I always knew you would get on well, you are so witty and elegant! God bless you! Fresh as a rose you are! What sheets and counterpane, and pillows all as white as snow! Ah, if only my old age were as happy as this! Now, my pearl, you shall see if I mean to do you a good turn when I visit you so late at night. Let me look at you! You're a sight for sore eyes!

AREUSA. No, no, don't touch me, I'm terribly ticklish. You make me laugh and that hurts.

CELESTINA. Hurts? My dear, you're joking!

AREUSA. May I be damned if I do! For the last four hours I've had a terrible pain in my belly. My breasts are all sore and tender. It's enough to kill me. I'm not as vicious as you seem to think!

CELESTINA. Let me look, let me feel you! I know all about it, for my sins! We poor women all suffer in this way in our time.

AREUSA. It hurts higher up, near the stomach.

CELESTINA. By God and blessed St Michael! My dear angel, how plump and appetizing you are! What breasts, what sweetness! I knew you were beautiful, seeing only what everyone sees, but now I may say that of all the bodies I know in this town, there are not more than three to compare with yours! You don't look a day over fifteen! He'll be a lucky man whom you allow to see all this! By God, you wrong those who love you in not letting them share such graces! God didn't give you these charms to languish in the freshness of your youth under half a dozen layers of linen! Don't be niggardly with what has cost you nothing, don't hoard your treasure! By its nature beauty is as communicable as coin! Don't be like the dog in the manger, and since you can't enjoy it yourself keep out those that can! Do you think you were created in vain? Was not woman made for man, man for woman? There is nothing useless in nature, nothing which does not depend on nature. It is a sin to make men sick with desire when one can cure their sickness.

AREUSA. Truly, mother, at the moment no one desires me. Give me something for my pain and don't make fun of me!

CELESTINA. I am afraid it is a pain we must all put up with, poor sinners that we are! I can tell you the remedies I've known others use and found generally successful. But everyone is different and may need different treatment. Any strong odour is good—pennyroyal, rue, wormwood, burnt feathers, rosemary, musk, incense. After a time the smell of these calms the nerves and soothes away the pain. But there is another way, which I have always found most successful. However, I don't like to suggest it to you, since you're being so pious to-day!

AREUSA. What is it, on my life, mother? You can see how ill I am! Why won't you help me?

CELESTINA. You know what I mean well enough! Don't play the innocent with me.

AREUSA. I understand you all right, a pox on it! But what can I do? My lover went off to the wars yesterday. Can I be unfaithful to him?

CELESTINA. Much harm that would do him!

AREUSA. It would do a lot of harm! He gives me everything I want, treats me with respect, looks after me just as if I were his wife.

CELESTINA. But in spite of all that you will suffer as you do now as long as you are not pregnant. And that is his fault! If to-night hasn't convinced you, think of the future, and then you will see what comes of living alone.

AREUSA. It's just my luck! My parents threw me out and I must get along as best I can. But never mind all that. It's late. Tell me why you came?

CELESTINA. You remember what I said about Parmeno? He complains that you won't even speak to him. I don't understand it! You know I am very fond of him and look on him as a son. I don't behave like that with you. I'm willing to be friends with anyone you are friendly with.

AREUSA. Truly, mother, I am not ungrateful.

CELESTINA. Actions speak louder than words! And words are cheap anyhow. Friendship should be repaid with friendship, and one good turn deserves another. You know you are cousin to Elicia, whom Sempronio keeps in my house. Parmeno is his fellow servant; they are both in the household of that young lord I told you about, who might be useful to you too. Don't refuse what I ask! It costs you little enough! You two girls are cousins, the two men are friends! See how well it all fits in! He came here with me. Can I tell him to come up?

AREUSA. My God, if he heard us talking!

CELESTINA. No, he's downstairs! Let me call him up! Make him happy by receiving him kindly, show him a smiling face! If you like him let him enjoy you! You won't lose by it and he'll gain much.

AREUSA. I know you are doing all this for my good. But you don't understand! How can I do as you ask? I've told you, there is someone to whom I owe everything, and if he hears of this he will kill me. My neighbours are spiteful, and they will be only too glad to tell him. I haven't much to lose, but even so I shall lose all I have if I do as you ask.

CELESTINA. I know all about the neighbours, and I was careful not to make a sound as we came in.

AREUSA. It isn't only to-night, but every night.

CELESTINA. So that's how it is? That is how you intend to

live? You will never get yourself settled in life! If you are so afraid of him when he is away, what would you be like if he were here in the city? Well, it's lucky for me that I am never tired of giving good advice to young fools, for there are plenty of them! The world is wide and there are few wise men in it! Ah, my daughter, if you could only see your cousin Elicia! She has known how to profit by my example and my good advice. What a woman she is! And none the worse for my lessons and a little rough handling now and then! She can always count on one in her bed, one at the door, and another sighing his heart out for her at home! She pleases them all, shows them all a smiling face, and makes each one think he is the beloved, he is the only one, he alone has her heart, and, having him, she has no need of anyone else! And you are afraid to take a second lover! Do you think the planks of your bed will betray you? Can you be satisfied with one dish? You intend to live frugally, I see! I wouldn't like to be dependent on your leavings! One was never enough for me! I was never one to put all my eggs in one basket! Two are better than one, four better still! The more there are the greater your profit, and the more choice you have! There is nothing more pitiful, my daughter, than a mouse with only one bolt-hole! If that's blocked up she doesn't know where to go to escape the cat. The one-eyed man is always in danger. A poor creature all alone neither laughs nor cries. A thing done once does not become a habit. How seldom you see a friar alone in the street; nor does the partridge fly alone! One soon tires of tasting a single dish. One swallow does not make a summer. One witness alone does not carry conviction. One dress is soon worn out. So what do you expect, my child, of one lover? I can think of more objections to it than I have years on my back. Take two, that's the least you can do. You have two eyes, two ears, two hands, two feet, two sheets on your bed, two chemises to your back! And if you have

more all the better! The more the merrier! Honour without profit is like a ring on the finger, and since you can't have
both take the profit and let the rest go hang! Come up, son
Parmeno!

AREUSA. No, don't call him up! Pox take me, I die of shame!
I don't know him! I shall blush to look at him!

CELESTINA. I'm here to help you. I'll smooth it over and
talk for two. For he is just as embarrassed as you!

PARMENO. Lady, God save your gracious presence!

AREUSA. Oh, sir, you are welcome!

CELESTINA. Come nearer, donkey! Why go and hide in the
corner? Don't be so shamefaced! Remember, the devil lies
in wait for the faint-hearted man! Now, listen to me, both of
you. You know, Parmeno, what I promised you, and you,
my daughter, what I asked you? I won't dwell on the trouble
I had to get you to agree! Long speeches would be out of
place. There is no time for them anyway! This lad is dying
of love for you, you know that well enough. You don't want
him to die, do you? I can assure you you won't find him too
bad if you let him pass the night here.

AREUSA. Oh, in God's name, mother, don't mention such a
thing! Sweet Jesu, don't ask me to do that!

PARMENO. Good mother, for the love of God, don't send me
away unsatisfied, for I am ready to die at the sight of her, I
love her so. Offer her all that my father left me! Tell her I
will give her everything I have! Go on, tell her, for she won't
look at me!

AREUSA. What is he whispering to you? Is he afraid I won't
do as you ask?

CELESTINA. He says, daughter, that he is happy to make your
acquaintance, for you are an honourable person and will not
refuse a small gift from him. Come here, oaf, boor, I want to
see what you are good for before I go. Go on, sport with her
in bed!

AREUSA. Surely he won't be so brazen as to come uninvited
into a private place?

CELESTINA. Get along with your invitations and private
places! I've no patience with you! I warrant he'll cure your
aches and pains by morning! He's a wanton, a cockerel, he's
just starting to grow a beard! I'll swear he's good for three
nights together! When I was young and had good teeth the
doctors in my country used to prescribe things like him for me
to crunch up!

AREUSA. Oh, sir, don't treat me so! Keep your distance, for
the love of God. Respect the white hairs of this honourable
old woman! Go away, I am not what you take me for. I
am not one of those who sell themselves for money! On my
life, I'll leave the house if you touch so much as my counterpane while Celestina is here.

CELESTINA. What's the matter, Areusa? Why all this fuss
and nonsense? This is a new fashion in love-making! You
seem to think, my dear, that I do not know what you are
doing! Do you suppose I have never seen a man and woman
in bed together before this? That I have never been in your
situation, or enjoyed what you are going to enjoy? That I
don't know what happens, or what is said and done? Alas,
few know better than I! Don't forget I was young once and
as much sought-after as you! But I never spurned the advice
of man or woman, in public or in private, or pushed them
from my side. By the death I owe God, I would sooner have
had a box on the ear! To listen to you one would think I
was born yesterday! You would like to appear honest by
making me out to be a fool and ashamed, a woman of no
experience and little value. But there's honour among
thieves! I praise you more behind your back than you
praise yourself in front of me.

AREUSA. Mother, if I have done wrong forgive me! Let him
come nearer and do as he pleases. I am more anxious to

please you than myself. I would rather pluck out my eyes than offend you.

CELESTINA. I am not offended, but I say this for the future! Now good-bye to both! I'll take myself off, for you set my teeth on edge with your kisses and caresses! I still have the taste of them in my mouth. I haven't lost that with my teeth!

AREUSA. God go with you!

PARMENO. Mother, shall I escort you home?

CELESTINA. That would be robbing Peter to pay Paul! God bless you, I am an old woman and not afraid of being set on in the street.

ELICIA. The dogs are barking. That means the old hag must be coming home.

CELESTINA. Rat-tat-tat!

ELICIA. Who is there? Who knocks?

CELESTINA. Come down and open the door, girl!

ELICIA. So you've come home at last! You seem to enjoy being out at night, I don't know why! Tell me, why are you out so late, mother? It's becoming a habit. To please one client you offend a hundred others. The father of that young girl has been here, looking for you—the one you took to the old canon on Easter Day. Her wedding is fixed for three days hence. You must put her right, as you promised, or her husband will soon know she's no virgin!

CELESTINA. I don't know who you are talking about, my dear!

ELICIA. You mean to say you don't remember? You must be out of your mind! You've a head like a sieve! You told me, before you took her, that you had already made a virgin of her seven times!

CELESTINA. I don't know why you're surprised at my bad memory! I have so much to think of, I can't remember everything. Tell me, is he coming back?

ELICIA. Coming back? Of course! He gave you a gold bracelet for your trouble. Don't you remember?

CELESTINA. Oh, the man with the bracelet! Yes, now I know who you mean. But why didn't you set to work and do the job? You ought to be able to do it by now, all the times you've seen me do it. Do you mean to spend the rest of your life in idleness, like an animal, when you've got a trade at your finger-tips? When you are my age you will be sorry you wasted your time. A lazy youth means a poverty-stricken old age. It was very different when your grandmother, God rest her soul, taught me all she knew. After a year I was better at it than she was!

ELICIA. That's not surprising, for they say the pupil often does better than the teacher. It all depends on how much you enjoy the work. Nobody learns anything unless they like it. You love the whole thing and I hate it, that's all.

CELESTINA. How can you say such a thing! Do you want to be poor when you are old? I shan't always be here to look after you.

ELICIA. Well, time will show! Let us not bother about it now. As long as we have enough to eat to-day, why worry about to-morrow? The rich man dies as soon as the beggar. We must all come to it, doctor or pastor, pope or priest, master or servant, high-born or low, you with your trade and I without! We can none of us live for ever. Let us enjoy ourselves while we can. Few of us see old age, and those that do will never die of hunger. All I ask in this world is a new day and a crust of bread, and my share of paradise! And though rich people have more chance of fame than poor ones, there isn't one who is content or says: 'I have enough!' There isn't one of them who wouldn't gladly exchange his money against my pleasures! Let us forget our cares and go to bed. It is late and a good sleep, without worrying, will do me more good than all the wealth of Venice!

ACT EIGHT

SUMMARY: *Day breaks. Parmeno wakes up, says good-bye to Areusa, and returns to his master's house. On the threshold he meets Sempronio and they exchange vows of friendship. They go together to Calisto's room and find him talking to himself. He gets up and goes to church.*

PARMENO. Is it morning already? Why is the room so light?

AREUSA. Morning? No! Go to sleep, my lord, we have only just gone to bed. I have not yet closed my eyes. Can it be morning already? Open those shutters beside you and we shall soon see.

PARMENO. I knew I was right, lady! It is broad daylight—I can see it through the crack in the door. Oh, what a disloyal servant I am! How shamefully I have behaved towards my master! I deserve to be punished! How late it is!

AREUSA. Late?

PARMENO. Very late!

AREUSA. And yet I don't feel any better. My sickness still torments me. I don't understand it.

PARMENO. What can we do about it, my love?

AREUSA. We must do something.

PARMENO. My dear, if what we have done already has been no good, you must forgive me if I decline to do anything further! It is already the middle of the morning, and if I stay much longer I shall get into serious trouble. I will come again to-morrow, and after that as often as you please. God always gives us another day to finish off what we have left undone!

But if you want to see me again to-day, come and join us all at Celestina's for the midday meal.

AREUSA. Very well, I will! Good-bye now, and close the door behind you.

PARMENO. Good-bye to you. Oh, ineffable pleasure, pleasurable joy! What man is as happy, or as fortunate, or as prosperous, as I? What a treasure I have got! No sooner asked for than yielded! Truly, if I could only find it in my heart to forgive the old woman's treachery, I would go on my knees to thank her! How can I ever repay her? Ah, God! To whom can I describe my joy? To whom confide my secret? Who make a partner in my happiness? The old hag was right! No pleasure is complete without a friend to share it. A hidden joy is no joy. Who is there to share the happiness I feel? There is Sempronio at the door of our house. He is up early! If my master is already awake he will be angry with me. But it is too early for that; he won't be up yet. Though if he has lost his senses he may well have altered his habits.

SEMPRONIO. Parmeno, my good lad, if I knew where I could earn good wages in my sleep I'd be glad! And I'd earn as much as the next man! You rascal, where did you get to last night? I don't know what you can have been up to, unless you stayed to keep the old woman warm, and tickle her toes, as you did when a boy?

PARMENO. Oh, Sempronio, my friend, dearer to me than a brother! Do not seek to spoil my pleasure; do not add to my remorse with your reproaches; do not destroy my happiness with your angry words; do not muddy the clear waters of my tranquillity, or darken my blue skies with your envy and railing! Receive me with open arms, and I will tell you of the wonderful thing that happened to me last night!

SEMPRONIO. Tell me, tell me! Is it anything to do with Melibea? Have you seen her?

PARMENO. Melibea? There is someone I love far better, someone, I flatter myself, who is her equal in beauty and elegance. For let me tell you, Melibea is not the only woman who is beautiful and elegant.

SEMPRONIO. What's all this, mad wag? I ought to laugh at you, but I can't! We are all in love and the world's run mad! Calisto loves Melibea, I love Elicia, and now you, envying our happiness, have found someone to steal away what little brains you were blessed with!

PARMENO. If it be madness to love, then let me be mad! Yet if this madness were painful, it would cry out from the roof-tops!

SEMPRONIO. You are mad, condemned out of your own mouth! Did I not hear you giving ridiculous advice to Calisto, contradicting Celestina, refusing your share of the profits of our enterprise, simply in order to send our plans awry? Oh, wretched creature, now I've got the laugh of you! I'll pay you out!

PARMENO. You would do better to help and advise me instead of ridiculing my passion. I have always looked on you as a brother. For the love of God, do not prove the truth of the old saying, that it takes only a trifling dispute to separate old friends! You always treat me unkindly—I do not know why. Do not seek to rouse me, Sempronio, with your cruel remarks. Be careful! Even my patience may not be proof against your sarcasm.

SEMPRONIO. I meant no harm. But God knows what children are coming to nowadays if even you have got yourself a mistress!

PARMENO. Now you are angry! Well, I must put up with it! They say nothing lasts for ever. But you are treating me very badly.

SEMPRONIO. You are treating Calisto very badly! You want him to do what you cannot do yourself, when you advise him to stop loving Melibea! You are like an inn sign that advises others to take shelter, and remains outside in all weathers! Oh, Parmeno, now you see how easy it is to blame others and how difficult to remain blameless! I'll say no more! You'll soon find out how it is, and then we shall see how well you manage when you're in it up to your neck like everyone else! If you had agreed to be my friend when I asked you, you would have helped me with our plans instead of trying to upset them. Just as bad wine drives drinkers from the inn, so adversity tries out the false friend and makes it easy to see the base metal under the gilding.

PARMENO. I have often been told, and now I know it to be true, that in our miserable existence there is no pleasure without pain. Our serene and happy days are darkened by clouds, winds, and rain. Our joy and our delight are accompanied by sorrow. Our laughter and mirth bring in their train tears and sighs and mortal groans. After rest and repose come grief and sadness. No one could have been happier than I was just now. No one more desolate than I am at present. I was happy in the fleeting pleasures of Areusa's bed. I have had a rude awakening. You will not let me tell you that I am your friend, that I am willing to help you, that I repent of the past, that the reproaches and good advice I have received from Celestina will benefit us all, and that since the conduct of our master's affair with Melibea lies in our hands, we must profit by it, now or never!

SEMPRONIO. I am glad to hear you say so. I only hope your deeds prove as good as your words. However, I am willing to believe you. But what was that you said about Areusa? Do you mean to tell me you know Areusa, Elicia's cousin?

PARMENO. Of course! Should I be so happy if I hadn't spent the night with her?

SEMPRONIO. Really, I can't help laughing at you! How foolishly you talk! Spent the night with her! I suppose you mean you talked with her at the window. Is that it?

PARMENO. I am wondering whether she is pregnant or not.

SEMPRONIO. You surprise me! So hard work was rewarded in the end? They say constant dripping wears away the stone!

PARMENO. It has not taken long. I thought of her yesterday morning and last night she was mine.

SEMPRONIO. I'll be bound the old woman had a hand in that!

PARMENO. What makes you think so?

SEMPRONIO. She told me she was very fond of you, and that she'd see you had everything you wanted. You were lucky! All you had to do was walk in and help yourself! Well, they say you never know your luck till the well runs dry! You must have been born under a lucky star!

PARMENO. No, but I had a good godmother! And they say: 'He who shelters under an oak will gather acorns!' I started late, but I soon caught up! Brother, I can't tell you what a wonderful woman she is, such a witty talker, and what a beautiful body! But that must wait for another time.

SEMPRONIO. Isn't she Elicia's cousin? You can't tell me anything about her I don't know already. I'll believe whatever you say. But how much did it cost you? Did you give her anything?

PARMENO. Nothing at all! But whatever it had cost it would have been worth it. She deserves the best. Such women are usually judged by their price. The more they cost the better you think them. But never did so rare a gift cost so little as Areusa. I have invited her to dinner at Celestina's. If you like we will all go together?

SEMPRONIO. Why, brother, who?

PARMENO. You and I and Areusa! Elicia and Celestina will be there already, and we shall all enjoy ourselves.

SEMPRONIO. Now, by God, boy, you warm the cockles of my heart! You are a good friend, and I don't care who hears me say so! You are a man now, God be thanked, and all my irritation with your chattering is turned to affection. Now I know you are one of us! Let me embrace you, let us be brothers, and we'll go to the devil together! The past is forgotten as if it had never been. Truly they say 'the falling out of faithful friends renewal is of love!' Let us eat, drink, and be merry. Our master fasts enough for us all!

PARMENO. And what is he doing, poor soul?

SEMPRONIO. He is in his room, lying on his bed—neither asleep nor awake—just as you left him last night. When I go in he snores; when I go out he shouts and raves. I can't make out whether he is happy or miserable.

PARMENO. He hasn't asked for me? Or remembered me at all?

SEMPRONIO. He hasn't enough sense to remember himself, let alone you!

PARMENO. He hasn't missed me? Then good luck was on my side. I may as well go and find something for dinner before he wakes up.

SEMPRONIO. What are you thinking of taking round with you? You want those giddy creatures to think you an accomplished, well-bred, generous youth!

PARMENO. In a rich household like this one can always find something to eat! A little of whatever there is won't come amiss! Some white bread, some Monviedro wine, a ham, and some of those young chickens our master's farmers brought in the other day. If he asks for them I'll make him believe he has already eaten them. And the pigeons he intended to have to-day—I'll say they were too high! You must back me up! We must make sure that what he eats of them won't hurt him! And there is our meal assured. And afterwards we must get the old woman to help us profit by his pleasure.

SEMPRONIO. Or his pain! For I think he will end up either dead or mad. And now that that is all settled let us go and see how he is!

CALISTO.   Alas, I faint, I fail,
            The hour of death draws near.
            I cannot hope to have
            Her whom I hold most dear.

PARMENO.   Do you hear that, Sempronio?   Our master is a poet!

SEMPRONIO.   A mad rhymster!   He thinks himself the equal of Antipater of Sidon and the great Ovidius Naso, whose thoughts sprang to their lips in verse.

PARMENO.   That is so!   The devil inspires him!   He raves between dreams.

CALISTO.   Heart, to your lonely grave!
            Calisto's joys are done.
            You were too quickly won
            To be Melibea's slave!

PARMENO.   Didn't I tell you he was inspired!

CALISTO.   Who is that in the other room?   Boys!

PARMENO.   Sir?

CALISTO.   What time is it?   Is it time to go to bed?

PARMENO.   It will soon be too late to get up.

CALISTO.   What do you mean, fool?   Is the night over?

PARMENO.   Yes, sir, and the best part of the day too!

CALISTO.   Tell me, Sempronio, he's lying, isn't he, this fool who wants to make me believe it's daylight?

SEMPRONIO.   Sir, if you could forget Melibea for a moment you would see for yourself that it is daylight.   You are so dazzled by the thought of her beauty, it blinds you as the lantern blinds the bird.

CALISTO.   Yes, you are right, it is day.   The bells are ringing for mass.   Give me my clothes!   I will go to church and pray God that Celestina may soften the heart of Melibea towards me, or else I will put an end to my miserable existence.

SEMPRONIO.   Sir, don't tire yourself out!   You can't do everything at once.   Sensible people don't rush to conclude

an affair which may end badly.   If you try to do a year's work
in a day you won't last long!

CALISTO.   You mean I am like the servant of the Galician
squire?

SEMPRONIO.   God forbid that I should say such a thing to my
master!   I know you would as soon punish me for evil speaking as reward me for good advice!   And truly they say that the
recompense of good service is not equal to the punishment
of bad!

CALISTO.   I did not know you were such a philosopher,
Sempronio!

SEMPRONIO.   Sir, a thing is not white because it is not black,
and all is not gold that glisters!   You are too impatient and
unreasonable to profit by my good advice.   Yesterday you
thought that at a word from you Melibea would be brought
here, bound hand and foot, as if she were some trifle from the
market-place that had only to be bought and paid for!   Console yourself, sir, with the thought that nothing worth having
is had so quickly!   One stroke of the axe will not fell an oak!
Bear your sufferings patiently, for patience is a praiseworthy
thing, and a man forewarned can resist the strongest attack!

CALISTO.   That would be excellent advice if my sufferings
allowed me to profit by it.

SEMPRONIO.   Where is your common sense, sir, if you allow
your desires to make you so unreasonable?

CALISTO.   Fool, fool!   The strong man says to the sufferer:
'God keep you in good health!'   I don't want your advice, or
your reasons, which only serve to excite and irritate the flames
which consume me.   I shall go alone to mass.   I shall not
come back until you fetch me, bringing good news from
Celestina.   Nor will I eat until the horses of Phoebus have
gone to those green fields where they rest after their day-long
journey through the sky.

SEMPRONIO.   Oh, sir, spare us these phrases, spare us the

poetry! What is the good of these extravagant expressions which no one else uses and few understand? Say—till sunset, and we shall know what you mean. But meanwhile eat at least a mouthful of fruit to give you strength till then.

CALISTO. Sempronio, my faithful friend, my good counsellor, my most loyal servant, it shall be as you please. For I am assured by your continual kind actions that you hold my life as dearly as your own!

SEMPRONIO. What say you, Parmeno? Would you swear to that? See if you can find the preserved fruit. Bring a second box for you know who. We can do with it! Slip it into your pocket.

CALISTO. What are you saying, Sempronio?

SEMPRONIO. Sir, I was just telling Parmeno to fetch you a slice of preserved melon.

PARMENO. Here it is, sir!

CALISTO. Give it to me!

SEMPRONIO. He eats as if the devil were after him! He would swallow it whole to get rid of it more quickly!

CALISTO. Ah, that's better! Go with God, my friends, find the old woman, and bring me good news from her!

PARMENO. To the devil with you and your love-affairs! I wish the preserved melon would serve you as the poison did Apuleius and turn you into an ass!

ACT NINE

SUMMARY: *Sempronio and Parmeno, deep in conversation, go to Celestina's house, where they meet Elicia and Areusa. They sit down to dinner, and during the meal Elicia quarrels with Sempronio. She gets up from the table. The others try in vain to calm her down. While they are all talking Melibea's maid Lucretia comes to ask Celestina to go to her mistress.*

SEMPRONIO. Parmeno, hand down our cloaks and swords! It is time we were off.

PARMENO. We must hurry or they will complain that we have kept them waiting. Not that way, this! We can look in at the church and see if Celestina has finished her prayers. If so, we can all go along together.

SEMPRONIO. I doubt if she will be saying her prayers at this time of day!

PARMENO. There is no special time for it. One can say a prayer at any time.

SEMPRONIO. That's true. But you don't know Celestina! When she is busy she has no time to spare for God or for holy thoughts. As long as there is enough to eat in the house she leaves the saints in peace. When she goes to church and tells her beads, that means supplies are low! Although she brought you up I know her better than you do. All she prays for is that she may undo many virgins, that the city may never lack young men in love, that many young girls may frequent her house, that the stewards may always remember her by name, so that she is not treated as a stranger, but given good wine— and plenty of it!—and that the canon may be ever young and generous! When her lips move she is concocting lies or thinking up ways of extorting money. 'I'll go to such a one, he'll say this, I'll reply that!' That's how our honoured old friend spends her time!

PARMENO. I know all that, and more besides. But I hesitated to say so, for you were angry with me when I said much the same thing to Calisto the other day.

SEMPRONIO. We know it privately, and take advantage of it, but to speak of it openly may be unwise. If our master finds out what Celestina is really like, he won't want to have anything more to do with her. He will employ someone else, someone we do not know, and we shall get none of the plunder, while Celestina, willingly or not, must share her gains with us.

PARMENO. That is well said! Now, be quiet, for here we are at the door and it is open. She's at home. Call out first in case they are changing their clothes and don't want to be seen.

SEMPRONIO. Come in! No need to bother about that! We are at home here. Ah, they are laying the table.

CELESTINA. Oh, my darlings, my little pearls of gold! May I always be as happy as I am now at the sight of you both!

PARMENO. The old woman lavishes endearments on us, brother! Beware of her false protestations!

SEMPRONIO. Never mind her, it's just her way. The devil only knows where she learnt it!

PARMENO. In need and poverty, in hunger, the best teacher in the world, the best sharpener of wits! What else teaches magpies and parrots to imitate our voices, to school their clever tongues to our words? Nothing but hunger!

CELESTINA. Girls, foolish wenches, come down, quickly! Here are two young men offering to do me violence!

ELICIA. I thought you were never coming. You certainly didn't hurry yourselves! My cousin has been here these three hours. It must be that lazy Sempronio who delayed you. He is never in a hurry to see me.

SEMPRONIO. Softly, my lady, my love, my life! He who serves another is not master of his time. So my situation

absolves me from all blame. Now, don't let us quarrel!
Come and sit down by me.

ELICIA. Yes, you're always ready to eat! There you sit, with
your clean hands and your black, wicked heart!

SEMPRONIO. We'll quarrel later! For the moment we'll
eat! Sit you down first, Mother Celestina.

CELESTINA. Sit down, children, there is room for us all. May
we have as much in paradise when we get there! Now, each
of you by his lady love! And I, who am all alone, will have
this cup and wine-jar beside me. They are all I have left to
keep me company. Now I am old I like nothing better than
to serve the wine! 'He who extracts the honey finds some
sticking to his fingers!' On winter nights there is no better
bedfellow than wine. Two jarfuls drunk last thing keep
me warm all night. And I double the dose as Christmas
approaches! Wine warms my old blood, strengthens me, keeps
me young and frolicsome. May I never be without it, for then
I have no fear of the future! As long as I have wine to drink a
crust of mouldy bread will last me three days. Wine soothes
our sorrows better than gold or coral. It gives courage to the
young man, strength to the old, puts colour in pale cheeks,
heartens the coward, quickens the sluggard. It comforts the
brain, keeps the stomach free from chills, sweetens the breath,
makes virile the impotent, helps to make work bearable, brings
the tired harvester out in a healthy sweat, cures the rheumatism
and the toothache, and travels unharmed by sea, which your
water won't do! It has more virtues than you have hairs on
your head. I don't know anyone who wouldn't sing its
praises! It has only one fault. If it is good it is expensive,
and if it is cheap it is nasty! So what's good for the body is
bad for the pocket. But in spite of that I always buy the best.
I drink so little, only about a dozen cupfuls at each meal; and
no one could make me drink more, except when I have guests
like to-day.

PARMENO. Mother, everyone says that three cupfuls at the most are salutary and sufficient.

CELESTINA. My son, they make a slight error in the figure! Thirteen, not three!

SEMPRONIO. Yes, yes, old lady, we all agree with you! But now let us eat and drink, or we shall barely have time to talk of our master's affairs, and of his beautiful and charming Melibea.

ELICIA. Get out of here, you graceless, shameless creature! Bad luck to what you have eaten and to this meal you have invited me to! I could part with the little I have had to hear you call that woman beautiful. Beautiful! That one beautiful? Jesu, Jesu! Your falsity disgusts and sickens me. That one beautiful! God damn me if I think so! What is there beautiful about her, the bleary-eyed bitch? God pardon your impudence and your ignorance! Who wants to waste time talking about her beauty and her charm? Melibea beautiful? She'll be beautiful when the moon's made of green cheese! Her sort of beauty can be bought at the barber's shop for tuppence! Why, I know half a dozen girls, living in this very street, whom God has dowered with more beauty than Melibea. If she seems beautiful it is only because she is beautifully dressed. Hang her clothes on a broomstick and you'd call that beautiful! Upon my life, though I ought not to say it, I think I am as beautiful as your Melibea!

AREUSA. And you haven't seen her as I have, my dear! God forgive me, if you saw her first thing in the morning it would take away your appetite! You wouldn't be able to stomach a morsel! Before she will let anyone see her face she shuts herself up in her room, and plasters it with unmentionable horrors, rubs it with honey and vinegar, with raw meat and rotten figs, and with other things I won't mention, seeing we are at table! That's what makes such women beautiful and beloved, not the graces of the body! And really, for such a young lady she has a remarkably large bosom—big enough to suckle triplets! A couple of enormous cabbages! I haven't seen her belly, but to judge by the rest it must be as slack as an old woman's of fifty! I don't know what Calisto sees in her. And to think that for her sake he neglects others whom he could have far more easily, and enjoy far more! But there, when the palate is corrupted sour things seem sweet!

SEMPRONIO. Well, we must speak as we find! But in the city everyone praises her.

AREUSA. Nothing is further from the truth than the opinion of the vulgar herd. You will never be happy if you take your ideas from them, for they are worthless! What they hate is good, what they like, bad! So do not judge of Melibea's grace and beauty by what the common people say!

SEMPRONIO. Lady, the common people are only too ready to find fault with their betters! If Melibea had faults they would have been discovered long ago by those who know her better than we do. And even if you are right, Calisto is a gentleman, Melibea well born. It is right and proper that such people should enjoy each other's company, and it is not surprising that Calisto should prefer Melibea to anyone else.

AREUSA. They say: 'Handsome is as handsome does!' We are all children of Adam and Eve, and should be esteemed for what we are, not for the virtues of our ancestors.

CELESTINA. Children, children, stop arguing! And you, Elicia, come and sit down and behave yourself.

ELICIA. Why blame me? It is all Sempronio's fault! How can I sit and eat my dinner beside him when he keeps telling me to my face that that slut of a Melibea is more beautiful than I?

SEMPRONIO. Now, my dear, you said it, not I! Comparisons are odious! It is all your fault, not mine at all.

AREUSA. Come, dear girl, sit down! Don't give the wretch the pleasure of upsetting you. Otherwise I shall have to leave the table too.

ELICIA. Well, for your sake I'll forgive him and do as he asks.

SEMPRONIO. Ha, ha, ha!

ELICIA. And what are you laughing about, may the pox take your lying lips?

CELESTINA. Don't answer her, my son, or we shall never come to the end of it! Let us attend to our own affairs! Tell me, how is Calisto? What was he doing when you left? How did you manage to get away together?

PARMENO. He's like a man under a spell, breathing fire, in despair, lost, half mad! He has gone to mass to pray God to help you in your enterprise, and he swears he won't come home until he hears that you have got the better of Melibea. So far we've got your silk dress and cloak, and my doublet. All the rest is moonshine! He may pay, or he may not!

CELESTINA. He'll pay all right when the time is ripe! After seed time comes the harvest! All is profit that comes easily, particularly when it comes from such a source, a man so rich that my poverty could be relieved by the crumbs that fall from his table. He won't suffer from his generosity—he suffers too much already from that which makes him generous! Those who are eaten up with lechery can see and feel and hear nothing else, and are beyond the reach of any other pain! Or so I judge, having known others not as infatuated and impatient as Calisto. They can't eat or drink or laugh or cry or sleep or wake or talk or be silent or suffer or rest; are neither happy nor miserable as long as the sweet perplexity of love's fiery passion fills their breasts. And when nature forces them to give way they do it blindly, so that when they would eat the hand forgets to lift the food to their mouths. If you speak to them you can never get a sensible answer. They are there in the body, but in spirit they are with their mistresses. Love is a strange thing! It can cross the earth, and the seas also, it is so strong. Its power is felt alike by men of very different temperaments. It surmounts all difficulties. It is a terrible thing, a fearful and redoubtable anxiety, which creates havoc everywhere. If you have ever loved, my children, you know I speak nothing but the truth!

SEMPRONIO. Lady, I agree with you entirely! And here sits the woman who made of me another Calisto, a lost, crazy creature, weary in mind and body. I dozed by day, stayed awake all night, gave myself up to all manner of monkey-tricks and foolishness—jumping over walls, risking my life every moment of the day, fighting bulls, breaking in horses, putting the weight, tilting with the lance, wearying my friends, breaking swords, climbing ladders, putting on armour, and a thousand other lover's follies: writing verses, composing couplets, inventing compliments. Yet it was all worth doing, since it won me such a jewel!

ELICIA. You seem very certain of having won me! Yet I tell you truly, no sooner had you turned your back than I found myself another lover, kinder and more courteous than you! He didn't spend his time provoking me, or leave me alone for a year, and then come home late and in a bad temper!

CELESTINA. My son, let her talk! She's angry now, but you may be sure the more she raves the more she loves you! All this is because you praised Melibea! She wants to pay you out in your own coin! I'll be sworn she longs for the meal to end, for then she will get what she so impatiently longs for! And we all know what that is! And as for her cousin, I know she thinks the same. Enjoy yourselves while you are young. He who waits in hope of better times repents later on. As I do now for many hours which I wasted in my youth, when I was loved and sought after! Now, for my sins, I am grown old and nobody wants me, though God knows I have great need of comfort! Kiss and make up, my children, for I have no pleasures now but in watching yours. While we are at table everything is permitted—from the waist up! Afterwards I'll not hinder you! The king could do no more! I know the girls won't accuse you of undue haste! Meanwhile poor old Celestina will champ her toothless jaws over the scanty remains of the feast! God bless you, my little pigeons, how you laugh, how happy you are! My little madcaps, my saucy rogues! That's the way to stop your quarrelling! Mind you don't knock the table over!

ELICIA. Mother, someone is knocking at the door! We shall be done out of all our sport!

CELESTINA. Go and see who it is, my child! It may be someone who will add to it!

ELICIA. Either I am deceived in her voice or it is my cousin Lucretia.

CELESTINA. Open the door, bring her in, she comes in a good hour! She has had a taste of what you want, though being in service stops her from enjoying herself as much as she would like.

AREUSA. On my life, that's very true, for those who serve a mistress have no time for pleasure and seldom taste the sweet fruits of love! They never see their kith and kin, their equals with whom they can chat freely and say: 'What did you have for dinner? Are you expecting? How many hens have you? Take me back to supper with you. Introduce me to your lover! How long is it since you saw him? How are you getting on with him? What are your neighbours like?' and suchlike matters. And oh, what a hard word, harsh and unpleasing, is that Madam! which they have always on their lips! That is why I have lived alone, ever since I was able to fend for myself. I can boast of having had no mistress but myself. You can waste the best years of your life in the service of the great ladies of to-day, and they repay the devotion of years with an old petticoat, all in rags! They swear at you, ill treat you, keep you under their thumbs until you hardly dare to open your mouth, and then, when the time comes for a girl to marry, they pick a quarrel with her, swear she has slept with the valet

or the son of the house, flirted with the husband or taken men
up to her room. They complain of a broken cup or a lost
ring, beat her and throw her out of doors, head over heels,
crying: 'Off with you, thief, wanton, before you destroy the
honour of my house!' So instead of presents she gets insults,
instead of marriage infamy, instead of a dowry and wedding
gifts she is bundled out naked and in disgrace. That's all
her profit, her hire, her salary! She is promised a husband,
and instead her very clothes are taken from her. The best
thing that can happen to her is to become a hanger-on of old
women, and run from one duenna to another with messages.
She is never called by her proper name, but always whore,
harlot: 'Where are you off to, fool? What have you been
doing, wretch? Why did you eat that, greedy? Do you call
that stove clean, sloven? Why haven't you brushed my cloak,
slut? What are you muttering, impertinent? Who broke the
plate, clumsy? Where is my towel, thief? You have given it
to your lover! Come here, creature, where is the sick hen?
Find her at once, or I'll stop the price of her out of your wages!'
And on top of all that a thousand boxes on the ear, scratched
faces, blows with a stick or the closed fist. Nothing you do is
right, nothing satisfies them. Their pleasure is in shouting,
they glory in losing their tempers. The best you can do is
worth nothing. So, mother, I would rather live alone in my
own small house and be my own mistress than dwell a prisoner
in rich palaces!

CELESTINA. You are right! You know what you are doing!
Wise men say: 'Better a dinner of herbs where love is than
a stalled ox and hatred therewith.' But say no more, for here
comes Lucretia.

LUCRETIA. Good day to you, aunt, and to all the company.
God bless you in your prosperity, honest folk!

CELESTINA. Prosperity, my daughter? What a thing to say!
Ah, you don't remember me in my palmy days, twenty years

ago and more! It would break anyone's heart to see me now
if they had known me then. I've seen the day, my dear, when
at this very table where your cousins are now sitting, there were
never less than nine young girls of about your age, for the
eldest was no more than eighteen and the youngest fourteen.
Well, that's life! The world wags on its way: some rivers run
dry, while others are in full spate. It is the law of nature;
nothing stays the same, everything changes! I could weep to
remember how I was respected once, and now, for my sins
and to my sorrow, everything is gone! As I grew older so I
declined, and my fortune diminished. The old saying is true:
'Everything must wax or wane, everything has its limits, everything its degrees.' My reputation reached its zenith, and
seeing how high it rose it is only natural that it should now
decline since I approach my latter end. I can judge by that
how little time is left me! Well I know that I rose to fall,
flowered to fade, was happy and am miserable. I was born
to live, lived to grow, grew to become old, became old to die.
And since I have known this for a long time I bear my mis-
fortunes patiently, though not entirely without repining, for I
am only flesh and blood after all!

LUCRETIA. You must have had a hard time with all those
young girls, mother! I don't suppose they were easy to manage.

CELESTINA. A hard time, my love? No, nothing but pleasure
and joy! They obeyed me, honoured me, respected me, never
crossed my will. I paid each what she was worth. They
never took a man without my permission. The ones that paid
well, whether lame or hunchbacked or one-armed, they
accepted without question, if I said so. Theirs was the labour,
mine the profit. While they were with me I never lacked
company. Young men, old men, boys, priests, dignitaries of
all kinds, from the bishop to the sacristan. When I went to
church caps were doffed to me as if I had been a duchess, and
those who did not salute me were considered poor creatures!

When I was half a mile off they all raised their eyes from their
prayer-books, hurried to see if I lacked anything, or to ask
after their particular treasure. When I approached them they
were so troubled, they didn't know what they were doing.
Some called me madam, some aunt, others my love, others
good old woman! They made assignations, either in my house
or in their own. Some gave me money, some promises, others
offered me presents of all kinds. One kissed the hem of my
cloak, another my cheek. All did me honour! And now I
am brought so low that you may say of me: She is just about
fit to cobble old shoes!

SEMPRONIO. I am surprised to hear such things of holy and
reverend men. Surely they were not all like that?

CELESTINA. No, indeed, my son, God forgive me if I lie to
you! There were many pious old folk who couldn't bear the
sight of me, and brought me little profit. But I think it was
mainly because they were jealous of the others. There were
so many priests, one found all kinds among them—some
chaste, some eager for what I had to sell. And I think there
are still plenty like that! They would send their squires and
menservants to escort me home, and hardly had I arrived than
there came to my door gifts of chickens and cockerels, geese,
ducks, partridges, turtle-doves, hams, pies, sucking-pigs.
Everyone sent me what they had received in tithes. And
afterwards they came in person to beg my acceptance of their
gifts, and to help eat them, in the company of my young girls.
And the wine! I always had some of the best wine in the city.
It came from many places—Monviedro, Luque, Toro, Madri-
gal, San Martin—so many that I forget their names, though I
remember their flavours well enough! But a poor old woman
has enough to do to get wine, without bothering where it
comes from! And there came also the priests without tithes.
They brought the loaves made from fine white flour that pious
women offered to the church. No sooner had it been blessed

than it was on my doorstep! Young men, straight and strong as marble pillars, came to my house bowed down with provisions. I don't know how I go on living as I do when I think of the old days!

AREUSA. For God's sake, mother, stop crying and moaning! We're here to enjoy ourselves. God will provide!

CELESTINA. How can I help crying when I remember the happy days and the life I used to lead, when I was loved by all and lacked for nothing? They always came to my house first if some pregnant woman took a whim for rare fruit out of season. They knew I would have the earliest and the best.

SEMPRONIO. Come, mother, it's no good dwelling on what's over and done with! You can't bring back the happy times, and you only make yourself miserable—and us! Let us go and enjoy ourselves while you deal with this young lady, who is waiting so patiently for your answer.

CELESTINA. Daughter Lucretia, why am I honoured by a visit from you?

LUCRETIA. Truly, mother, hearing you talk of the past has quite made me forget my errand! I could sit happily for hours thinking of the wonderful life your young girls must have led. I can almost imagine I am one of them. But the reason for my visit, good mother, if you must know, is to ask you for the girdle. And also my mistress begs you to go and see her, for she is very weak and ill with heart trouble!

CELESTINA. My dear, I don't think there can be anything seriously wrong with her! She is rather young to suffer with her heart!

LUCRETIA. (The devil take you, you false hag! You know very well what I mean. You come and make mischief, then go off and pretend you know nothing about it!)

CELESTINA. What's that, daughter?

LUCRETIA. Mother, for God's sake come, and bring the girdle!

CELESTINA. I have it here. Come, we'll go together!

ACT TEN

SUMMARY: *While Celestina and Lucretia are on their way Melibea talks to herself. When they arrive Lucretia enters first, and then ushers in Celestina. In the course of conversation Melibea confesses to Celestina that she is madly in love with Calisto. They see Alisa, Melibea's mother, coming and separate at once. Alisa asks her daughter what Celestina wanted, and forbids her to see the old woman again.*

MELIBEA. Oh, how unhappy I am! How imprudently I have acted! Would it not have been better to agree to Celestina's demand when she first came to me from that young lord whom I loved as soon as I saw him? That would have pleased him and eased me. And now I am forced to declare my passion when perhaps he no longer desires me. Who knows? Despairing of a favourable reply, he may already have looked elsewhere. How much happier he would have been to possess me when he first desired me, than now, when I must offer myself to him! O faithful Lucretia, what will you say, what will you think of me, when I publish abroad this folly which I would not confess even to you? How horrified you will be to see me cast aside that modesty which I have hitherto preserved as a well-brought-up young lady should! I do not know if you have guessed the secret of my grief. Oh, if I could but see you coming with the old woman who alone can comfort me! O sovereign Lord, Thou whom all unhappy ones implore, Thou from whom the anguished soul seeks succour and the sick soul remedy, Thou whom the sky, sea, earth, and infernal regions obey, Thou who hast rendered

subject to man all things here below, humbly I beg, grant my
sad heart strength and patience to hide its sufferings! Let me
not tear aside the chaste veil which hides my amorous desires!
Help me to conceal my malady, or ascribe it to some other
cause! Yet how can I, suffering as I am from the cruel wound
dealt me by the bright eyes of that peerless youth? Alas, poor
women! How weak and frail we are! Why may not we
confess our deep and lasting love as freely as men do? If
that were possible Calisto would have no cause of complaint,
and I should be freed from this torment!

LUCRETIA. Aunt, wait outside while I see who is talking with
my mistress. Oh, you can come in, she is all alone!

MELIBEA. Lucretia, close the door! Wise and honourable
old lady, you are welcome! My destiny and my good fortune
have decreed that I should find myself in need of your advice.
Now I must ask of you the help you begged of me for that
young man whom you hoped to cure by virtue of my girdle.

CELESTINA. What is your complaint, lady? For I see by the
whiteness of your cheeks that you suffer terribly!

MELIBEA. Good mother, serpents sting and feed upon my
heart!

CELESTINA. (Good, good! All goes as well as I could wish!
I'll pay you out, young woman, for your impertinence
to me!)

MELIBEA. What is that you say? Have you guessed already
the cause of my malady?

CELESTINA. You have not yet told me the symptoms, lady.
How then should I guess the cause? All I can say is that I am
sorry to see you so altered. You have quite lost your looks.

MELIBEA. Give them back to me, good old woman! You
have already made proof of your powers.

CELESTINA. Lady, wisdom belongs to God alone. But for
the healing and cure of the sick, men have been allowed to
discover medicines, some by experience, some by study, some

by instinct. This poor old woman has been accorded a little of the last grace. What she knows is at your disposition.

MELIBEA. Oh, how happy I am to hear you say so! The doctor's smiling face brings immediate relief to the poor sufferer! I seem to see my broken heart already in your hands, mended by the power of your words alone; even as the great Alexander, king of Macedonia, dreamt he saw in the mouth of a dragon the healing herb which cured his friend Ptolemy of a snake bite. For God's sake take off your cloak, sit down comfortably, and let us talk of my malady, which I am sure you can cure.

CELESTINA. He who wishes to be well is half way to health! Which makes me think that you are in no danger of death, daughter! Yet before, by the grace of God, I give you healing medicines, you must tell me three things. First, in which part of your body is the pain most tenacious and penetrating? Secondly, how long have you been troubled with it? For it is easier to cure a malady in its early stages than after it has become lodged in the body. Animals are more easily tamed in youth, before their skin toughens and becomes less sensible to the prick of the goad. Plants which are transplanted when they are young and tender take root more easily than those that have already borne fruit. It is easier to correct a new fault than one that has become a daily habit. The third thing I must know is, does the pain proceed from some recent unhappiness? When I know all this I can act. But remember that to your doctor, as to your father confessor, you must tell the whole truth!

MELIBEA. Friend Celestina, in your wisdom and experience you show me clearly the way to confide in you in this matter. Certainly you speak like one very experienced in tending such ills. My suffering comes from the heart. It is centred in my left breast, and from there it extends to all parts of my body. Secondly, it is quite recent. I never thought pain could so torment me.   It has ruined my looks, taken away my appetite, prevented me from sleeping, stopped me from enjoying anything.   As for your last question, I cannot call to mind any recent unhappiness—no death in the family, no loss of wealth, no troubled nights, no bad dreams.   I cannot think of anything, unless it be the distress I felt when I suspected that the prayers you asked of me were only a ruse to conceal some wicked design on the part of that young man.

CELESTINA.   Lady, why do you think so badly of him?   Is his name so terrible that only to hear it pronounced deals you a mortal blow?   You must not think that he is the cause of your malady.   I suspect something else, and if you will permit me, madam, I will tell you what it is.

MELIBEA.   Why, Celestina, what nonsense is this?   Do you need my permission to cure me?   Does the doctor ask permission before healing his patient?   Speak, speak, I permit anything, as long as you do not touch my honour.

CELESTINA.   I see, lady, that while you complain of pain you nevertheless fear the remedy!   Your hesitation makes me afraid, fear keeps me silent, silence comes between your illness and my remedies.   So you will not be cured and my visit here will have been in vain.

MELIBEA.   The longer you delay the worse I feel.   Either your medicines are infamous powders and corrupting liquors, which make the patient worse than he was, or else your boasted wisdom is naught.   If it is not so tell me freely what is in your mind.   I beg you to speak, and only ask you to be careful of what touches my good name.

CELESTINA.   Madam, you know that it is harder for the wounded man to endure the sting of the terebine and the sharp prick of the needle which stitches his wound than it was for him to suffer the pain of the first infliction of that wound, when he was in good health.   So, if you wish to be cured, and will fearlessly endure the prick of my needle, bind your hands and feet with the cords of tranquillity, your eyes with the bandage of patience, your mouth with the bridle of silence, your ears with calm and constancy, and then you will see an old woman act who is skilled in such wounds.

MELIBEA. Oh, your delays kill me by inches! For God's sake say what you like, do what you can, for your remedy, however painful, cannot equal my torment and despair! Even if it touches my honour, even if it damages my reputation, even if it wounds my body, even if you have to open my breast and tear out my grieving heart, I promise to let you do it. And if I feel better for it I will reward you handsomely!

LUCRETIA. (My mistress has lost her reason! She is ill indeed! The wretched old crone has bewitched her!)

CELESTINA. (I seem fated to meet the devil to-day, whichever way I turn! God has delivered me from Parmeno and afflicted me with Lucretia!)

MELIBEA. What are you saying, dear mother? What did the girl say to you?

CELESTINA. I did not hear what she said. Let her say what she will! But you must know that in these cases there is nothing more trying to the zealous surgeon than these coward hearts! Their sighs, their sympathy, their flinchings, which frighten the patient and make him despair of recovery, also irritate and annoy the doctor. Their presence makes his hand unsteady, and so the needle goes awry. If you are to get well we must have no one in the room with us. Tell her to go! You, I mean, daughter Lucretia, if you will forgive me!

MELIBEA. Leave us at once!

LUCRETIA. Alas, all is lost! I go, lady!

CELESTINA. Your fortitude encourages me, for I see that in spite of your suspicions you have already begun to take my medicine! But I must fetch the strongest and the best from the house of the young gentleman Calisto!

MELIBEA. Oh, God, mother, be silent! Do not fetch anything

from his house for my benefit! Do not even name him to me!

CELESTINA.   Lady, you must suffer patiently the first and most vital prick of the needle! Do not flinch, otherwise all our labour is in vain. Your grief is great: it needs a powerful remedy. Strength must be pitted against strength if it is to be overcome. Wise men say that the ruthless surgeon gets the best results, and no risks can be avoided without taking further risks! Be patient! Nothing troublesome is cured without trouble! As one nail drives out another, so one pain replaces another. Do not be so proud and disdainful! Do not stoop to speak ill of one as virtuous as that worthy gentleman! If you but knew him!

MELIBEA.   Oh, God, you are killing me! Have I not forbidden you to praise him, or even to mention him, whether for good or ill?

CELESTINA.   Lady, that is a second painful prick! If you cannot bear it I am wasting my time here. If you will only be patient, as you promised, you will soon be cured and no longer in debt, Calisto above reproach and well repaid! I warned you of all this, and of the invisible pricks which you would feel at the mere mention of his name!

MELIBEA.   You mention it so often that in spite of my promise, in spite of my faith in your remedies, I cannot bear it patiently! What debt do I owe him? Why must he be repaid? How am I bound to him? What has he done for me? What can he do to cure my malady? I had rather you cut me open and tore out my heart than have to listen to such speeches.

CELESTINA.   Love's dart pierced your heart without tearing your garments! To tear your flesh will not cure the smart of it!

MELIBEA.   What do you call this pain which has so taken prisoner the best part of my body?

CELESTINA.   Sweet love!

MELIBEA. Ah, even to hear it spoken of makes me feel better!

CELESTINA. It is a hidden fire, a wondrous wound, a savoury poison, a sweet bitterness, a delightful grief, a joyful torment, a kind yet cruel hurt, a pleasing death!

MELIBEA. Oh, unhappy that I am! If what you say is true my recovery is impossible. For, by the opposition of these qualities, what is good for one will be fatal to the other!

CELESTINA. Do not despair, my dear young lady! Where God inflicts the wound He gives also the remedy! I know a flower in this world which will cure you at once!

MELIBEA. What flower is that?

CELESTINA. I dare not name it.

MELIBEA. Speak, and fear not!

CELESTINA. Calisto! Oh, God, sweet lady Melibea, what weakness is this? What faint-heartedness? Oh, wretch that I am! Lift up your head! Oh, miserable old fool! This is the result of all my meddling! If she dies they will kill me. If she recovers she will disclose the cause of her sorrow and the remedy I proposed. Lady Melibea, my angel, what is the matter? Have you lost your voice? Where has your colour fled? Open your lovely eyes! Lucretia, Lucretia, come quickly! Your young lady has fainted away in my arms. Bring water!

MELIBEA. Softly, softly! I shall soon be well. Do not rouse the house!

CELESTINA. Oh, have pity on me! Do not swoon again! Speak to me, lady! Let me hear your voice!

MELIBEA. I am better now. Leave me alone, do not bother me!

CELESTINA. What shall I do, my precious pearl? What caused your qualms? I fear my stitches have burst!

MELIBEA. It was my heart that burst! My honour is impugned, my modesty outraged, my pride in the dust! They have been part of me so long they could not leave me suddenly

without taking my colour, my strength, my speech, and the
greater part of my five wits!   And now, good mother, faithful
confidant, now that you know my secret it is useless for me to
try to hide it.   Many days have passed since that noble gentleman first spoke to me of love.   His words wounded me as
much as your praise of him has since delighted me.   Your
needle has stitched up my wound.   I will do as you bid me.
You have taken away my liberty tied up in my girdle.   Calisto's
toothache was my worst pain; his sufferings my most cruel
agony.   I cannot praise too highly your patience, your
courage, your audacity, your generosity, your loyalty, your
dispatch, your wisdom, your kindness, and your ceaseless
importunity.   He owes you much, and I even more.   My
reproaches have been powerless to shake your firmness and
perseverance.   You stood firm in your wisdom.   Like a
devoted servant, the more I scolded the greater your diligence,
the more I raged the greater your determination.   When I was
angry you smiled; when I threatened you submitted.   You
questioned me without fear, and you have torn from my breast
a secret that I thought never to have shared with anyone!

CELESTINA.   Dear lady, do not be surprised! The certainty of
success gives me courage to bear the reproaches and overcome
the scruples of such delicately nurtured young ladies as yourself!   It is true that on my way here, and even once I was in
the house, I was in two minds whether to do my errand or not.
Remembering your father's power, I trembled; thinking of
Calisto's merit, I took courage.   Questioning your discretion,
I hesitated; mindful of your goodness and humanity, I went
forward.   Fear held me back, confidence drove me on.   And
now, lady, that you have confessed your inclination towards
Calisto, tell me what you want, pour your secrets into my
bosom, put your affairs into my hands!   I will see that your
desire and that of Calisto is fulfilled without delay.

MELIBEA.   O Calisto, my lord and my love, my sweet and

pleasant joy! If your heart feels as mine does now, I marvel that absent from me you still contrive to exist! O good mother and most dear lady, if you value my life let me see him soon!

CELESTINA. You shall see him and speak to him.

MELIBEA. Speak to him? Impossible!

CELESTINA. Nothing is impossible to those who are determined to succeed.

MELIBEA. But tell me how?

CELESTINA. I have thought of a way and I will tell you! Within the walls of your own house!

MELIBEA. When?

CELESTINA. To-night!

MELIBEA. If you succeed in this I shall never be able to thank you enough! At what time?

CELESTINA. Midnight!

MELIBEA. Then go, my lady, my most loyal friend! Speak to my lord; tell him to come silently, and if he agrees we will meet as you suggest at the hour you mention.

CELESTINA. Adieu, for here comes your mother.

MELIBEA. Friend Lucretia, my loyal servant and faithful confidant! You see I could not help myself! I am led captive to the feet of Calisto! I beg you, in God's name, to keep my secret, so that I may enjoy the sweets of love! If you do this I will reward you as you deserve.

LUCRETIA. Madam, I knew what ailed you long ago, and felt pity for you in your sufferings. I was sorry to see you in such danger. The more you tried to hide the fire which consumed you, the more I recognized it for what it was by the pallor of your cheeks, the beating of your heart, the trembling of your limbs, your lack of appetite, your sleeplessness! Every moment of the day I could see clearly what was the matter with you. But when the mistress is the victim of an irresistible passion, the poor servant can only show diligence and obedience, refrain from proffering unwelcome advice, submit patiently, keep silent, and remain steadfast in dissembling. Though truly I believe that good counsel is worth more than smooth-faced flattery! But since your ladyship desires nothing better than to love and die for love, we must be patient and take what comes!

ALISA. What are you doing here again to-day, neighbour?

CELESTINA. Madam, the thread I sold you yesterday lacked something of its full weight. So I have brought the rest to-day, as I promised. I have kept my word, and now I am going. God be with you!

ALISA. And with you also! Daughter Melibea, what did the old woman want with you?

MELIBEA. She wanted to sell me a lotion for the face.

ALISA. That is more likely than the tale she told me, the old witch! She guessed I would not approve and so lied to me. Beware of her, my daughter, she is not to be trusted! Thieves are always prowling round rich men's houses! With her plots and stratagems, and her false merchandise, she can corrupt the most virtuous women and cause them to lose their reputations. If she is seen to enter a house more than once all the tongues begin to wag!

LUCRETIA. Our mistress has left it too late!

ALISA. For my sake, daughter, if she comes here without my knowledge, do not receive her or make her welcome. Answer her in all honesty and she will never come back. True virtue is more to be feared than the sword!

MELIBEA. Is she really so dangerous? Then I will not admit her again. Thank you, dear mother, for warning me of the dangers I must avoid!

ACT ELEVEN

SUMMARY: *After leaving Melibea Celestina walks along talking to herself. She sees Sempronio and Parmeno, who are going to the church of St Mary Magdalene to meet their master. Sempronio speaks to Calisto. Celestina arrives. They all go to Calisto's house, where Celestina tells him what has happened and receives her reward. During this time Sempronio and Parmeno talk together. Celestina leaves Calisto and goes home. She knocks at the door, Elicia opens it, and they eat and go to bed.*

CELESTINA. Dear God, how shall I ever get home, so freighted as I am with good news! There are Parmeno and Sempronio going into the church. I will follow them. If we meet Calisto we can all go to his house, and then I can claim my reward for the good news I bring him.

SEMPRONIO. Sir, the world wonders that you stay so long in church! Be advised by me and do not get yourself talked about. Nowadays the over-pious are called hypocrites! Everyone will say that you weary the saints with your petitions. If you must pray do it at home, not before all the world. Do not let them see you suffer, for the remedy lies in hands that will not fail you.

CALISTO. Whose hands?

SEMPRONIO. Celestina's!

CELESTINA. Who speaks of Celestina? What says this slave of Calisto's? I have been following you from the end of the road, but my wretched petticoats prevented me from catching you up.

CALISTO. O jewel of the world, easer of my pain, mirror of

127

my joy, my heart rejoices in your honest presence, your noble old age! Tell me, whence come you? What news do you bring? Your looks speak of joy, and yet I know not where my joy may be found.

CELESTINA. In my mouth!

CALISTO. What say you, my glory and my repose? Tell me plainly, what do you mean?

CELESTINA. Sir, let us leave here, and on the way home I will tell you something that will certainly make you joyful.

PARMENO. The old woman looks pleased, brother! She must certainly be the bearer of good news.

SEMPRONIO. Let us hear what she has to say.

CELESTINA. All day, sir, I have been running about on your business, to the detriment of other affairs more important to me. I displease many to please you! I have lost more by it than you realize. But all comes in a good hour, for I bring wonderful news. Listen, and I will tell you all! Briefly, Melibea is yours!

CALISTO. What do I hear?

CELESTINA. She is more yours than her own, more yours to command than her father Pleberio's!

CALISTO. Be serious, mother, do not mock me! These lads will think you are mad! Melibea is my lady, Melibea is my divinity, Melibea is my life! I am her prisoner, her slave!

SEMPRONIO. Sir, all this modesty, this mistrust, this lack of confidence in yourself, leads you to talk wildly. People will laugh at you if they hear you say such things! Why are you so taken aback? You would do better to give the old woman something for her trouble, for that is what she expects!

CALISTO. Well said! Mother, I know I can never repay you for all the trouble you have taken on my behalf. Instead of a mantle and a silk dress—of which the tailors must have their share!—take this little chain. Hang it round your neck, and now, tell me more of my happiness!

PARMENO. Little chain, he calls it! Do you hear that, Sempronio? He doesn't know its value! I tell you truly, I won't take less than a gold piece for my share when the time comes for the old woman to pay up!

SEMPRONIO. If he hears you it will take us all our time to calm him down, and you won't get off lightly either! He is already incensed by your continual muttering! For my sake, brother, listen and be silent, for which purpose God gave you two ears and only one tongue!

PARMENO. He hear me? He's blind and deaf and dumb, hanging on the lips of that old woman! He is like a madman. If we were to point our fingers at him in scorn, he would only think we were raising our hands to heaven to pray for his success!

SEMPRONIO. Be quiet and hear what Celestina says. Upon my word, she deserves all he gives her, and more! She speaks well!

CELESTINA. Lord Calisto, you have behaved generously to a poor old woman. And since the value of any gift is greater or less according to the merit of him who gives it, I will not speak of my unworthiness, which you so far surpass in quality and quantity, but praise you for your munificence, before which I am as nothing! In return for your liberality I will give you back your health, which you were in danger of losing, your heart, which you thought lost indeed, and your reason, which everyone else has believed lost! Melibea suffers more for love of you than you for love of her! She adores you and longs to see you. She thinks of you constantly. She calls herself yours, and holds that a title to freedom, with which she calms the flames that burn her more than they burn you!

CALISTO. Friends, do I hear aright? Lads, are you with me? Am I awake? Is it day or night? O God, Heavenly Father, let it not be a dream! Yes, I am awake! If you mock me, lady, with lying words, confess it frankly, without fear! If you speak truth, all you have received from me is nothing in comparison with what you deserve.

CELESTINA.   A heart tormented with love will never take good news for certain, nor bad news for doubtful!   Yet whether I mock you or not you can prove by going this very night—as I have concerted with her—to Melibea's house as the clock strikes twelve.   And there you may talk to her through the door.   You will hear from her own mouth, better than I can report it, my pleading and her desire, the love she bears you, and how it began.

CALISTO.   Enough, enough!   Dare I hope for that?   Can such happiness be mine?   I shall die before to-night!   I cannot support such joy, I do not merit such a recompense. I am not worthy to speak to such a lady, even at her own wish.

CELESTINA.   I have often heard it said that it is more difficult to bear good fortune than bad, for the latter can be accepted with resignation, but the former can never satisfy!   Why, lord Calisto, remember who you are, remember the time you have spent in her service, remember too who has charge of this affair!   Until now you have always been doubtful of success, you have been in the depths of despair!   But now that I tell you your uncertainty is at an end you talk of dying! Think, think, sir, that Celestina is on your side!   Even if you lacked all the qualities essential in a lover, she would still make you out to be the most perfect gallant in the world, she would flatten the mountains before you, and carry you over raging torrents without wetting the sole of your shoe!   Little do you know whom you have taken into your service!

CALISTO.   Tell me again, good mother!   She comes of her own free will?

CELESTINA.   She would come on bended knees!

SEMPRONIO.   I hope this is not a trick to get us all in her power!   Be careful, mother!   That's how one wraps up rat poison, so as to disguise the taste!

PARMENO. You never spoke a truer word! I too feel rather suspicious of this young lady's sudden capitulation! Could she come so quickly under Celestina's spell? Perhaps she tricks us with honeyed words to rob us unaware, as gipsies do when they pretend to read your fortune in your hand. For truly, mother, many falsities are masked by flattery. The piping cry of the decoy lures the partridge into the net; the false siren's song leads astray the unwary mariner. Even so, by pretending to yield to you, Melibea may be trying to lure us to her, and to avenge the insult to her innocence by the loss of Calisto's honour and by our deaths. Like the new-born lamb, who, so long as he is fed, does not care whether his milk comes from his dam or from some stranger ewe, so Melibea may hope to take vengeance safely on all of us. With so many servants at her command, she could take master and men in one fell swoop, while you sit snugly by the fire, saying: 'He who sounds the alarm bell is safe in the belfry!'

CALISTO. Quiet, wretch, fool, suspicious idiot! Would you make me believe that angels can do wrong? For Melibea is an angel, who dwells among us in disguise!

SEMPRONIO. (Back to your old tune!) Listen to him, Parmeno! But don't worry! If there is treachery he'll pay for it. You and I can take to our heels!

CELESTINA. Sir, you are right! Your servants are boobies, stupid, suspicious fools! I have done my duty, so I leave you to your happiness. God keep you, sir, I am quite content with what I have. If you need me again, for this or for any other little affair, I am always at your service.

PARMENO. Ha, ha, ha!

SEMPRONIO. What are you laughing at now?

PARMENO. To see how fast the old crone hurries off with her booty! She wants to get her gold chain safely home. She still can't believe he really gave it to her, and that it is hers in good earnest.   She thinks herself as unworthy of such a jewel as Calisto thinks himself of Melibea!

SEMPRONIO.   What do you expect of an old whore like that, an old bawd who knows and understands all that we try to hide, and mends seven virginities for tuppence?   She has got a good store of gold now, and she is in a hurry to get it safely hidden away, for fear it may be taken from her, now that she has done all that was required!   But let her beware of the devil, for when the time comes to share our gains I'll have my part, or her life shall answer for it.

CALISTO.   God be with you, good mother!   Now I will go to bed, to make up for many sleepless nights, and prepare for those still to come!

CELESTINA.   Rat-a-tat-tat!

ELICIA.   Who is there?

CELESTINA.   Open up, daughter Elicia!

ELICIA.   Where have you been all this time?   You ought not to stay out so late at your age!   You might stumble in the dark, fall down and die in the street!

CELESTINA.   I am not afraid of that!   Before I go out at night I pick my way by daylight.   I never go to one side or the other, but always keep in the middle of the road, for as they say: 'He goes not safely who goes by the wall, and he goes safely who crosses the plain!'   I would rather dirty my shoes in the mud than have a stone fall on my head!   But you must have been having a miserable time, my dear!

ELICIA.   Why should I?

CELESTINA.   Because your friends left you here all alone.

ELICIA.   Oh, that was hours ago!   I have already forgotten it!

CELESTINA.   The earlier they left the worse for you!   But never mind that now.   Let us have supper and then go to bed.

ACT TWELVE

SUMMARY: *At midnight Calisto, Sempronio, and Parmeno, all armed, go to Melibea's house. Lucretia and Melibea are waiting for Calisto behind the door. He arrives. Lucretia speaks to him first, then calls Melibea and leaves them together. They talk through the door. Meanwhile Parmeno and Sempronio talk together. They hear a noise in the street and get ready to leave. Calisto says farewell to Melibea, after arranging to meet her again the next night. Pleberio, hearing a noise outside, wakes up and calls his wife Alisa. He asks Melibea why there are footsteps in her room. She lies to him, saying she felt thirsty. Calisto returns home, talking to Sempronio and Parmeno, and goes to bed, while they go to Celestina's house to demand their share of the booty. She refuses to give them anything. They get angry, draw their swords, and kill her. Elicia screams and the watch comes to arrest both men.*

CALISTO. What time is it, lads?

SEMPRONIO. Ten o'clock.

CALISTO. Oh, how badly I am served by these lazy rogues! I have been watching all night, while they have been idling and dozing. Brainless idiot! You know how important it is that I should be punctual to-night. Why then answer carelessly the first thing that comes into your head? What would have happened if I had gone to sleep and depended on Sempronio to wake me, when for eleven he says ten, and for twelve would have said eleven? Melibea would have been there to meet me, and when I failed to arrive she would doubtless have gone away and refused to see me again. So all my labour would have been in vain and my desire still unfulfilled.   Truly they say: 'Man's happiness hangs by a hair!'

SEMPRONIO.   I think it is as bad to ask a question, knowing the answer, as to reply wrongly through ignorance.   Surely, sir, it would be better to spend the hour that yet remains to us in looking to our weapons, rather than in asking silly questions?

CALISTO.   (The fool counsels wisely!   I must not let myself be angry now.   I must not think of what might have been, but of what has been; not of the harm which might have resulted from his negligence, but of the good that has come from my vigilance.   I must try and restrain myself, overcome my bad temper, and cease to feel annoyed.)   Parmeno, give me my cuirass and arm yourselves.   Then we shall be safe, for they say: 'Well armed is half the battle!'

PARMENO.   Here you are, sir.

CALISTO.   Help me to put it on!   Sempronio, look out and see if there is anyone about.

SEMPRONIO.   No one at all, sir.   And even if there were it is too dark for us to be seen or recognized.

CALISTO.   Then let us go!   This way!   It is a little out of our way, but we are less likely to meet anyone.   Midnight strikes! How bravely it sounds!

PARMENO.   We are almost there.

CALISTO.   We have come in a good hour.   Prepare yourself, Parmeno; see if my lady is behind the door!

PARMENO.   I, sir?   God forbid that I should interfere in the arrangements!   It would be better for you to be the first person she sees.   If she knows I am here she may be angry, judging that her secret is shared among many.   She will take fright and may think you send me to make sport of her.

CALISTO.   Well bethought of!   You give me new life with this good advice, for it would be enough to kill me stone dead if by any unlucky chance I failed to meet her here.   I will go alone.   Wait here, both of you!

PARMENO. What do you think of that, Sempronio? Our fool of a master wanted to use me as a shield and send me before him into danger! How do I know who is behind that door? There may be treason afoot! Suppose Melibea is planning to punish our master for his audacity? I am not yet convinced that the old hag told him the truth. If you didn't know how to take care of yourself, my poor Parmeno, they would steal the soul from your body without your knowing it! Do not be a flatterer, as your master wishes, and then you will not have to weep for another man's woes! Do not heed the advice and admonitions of Celestina, and then you will be safe! Do not make too many protestations of loyalty, or you may be cudgelled! Know that discretion is the better part of valour if you wish to sleep quietly at night. I look on this as the beginning of a new life, for I have just escaped from a mortal danger.

SEMPRONIO. Softly, softly, Parmeno! Do not jump for joy and make such a noise or you may be heard.

PARMENO. Hold your tongue, brother! I have good reason to jump for joy. Did you see how I made him believe it was for his sake I sent him in first, when all the time it was to save my own skin? I can look after myself! None better! If you observe me carefully in future you may see me do many strange things which will not be understood by Calisto and the others engaged in this business, for I think this lady is like fish bait, or poisoned meat, and those who are caught by her will pay dearly for it!

SEMPRONIO. Go to, you are wrong to harbour such suspicions, even if they are true! But if you hear a noise be ready to show a clean pair of heels, like the men at Villadiego who ran off with their breeches in their hands!

PARMENO. I have read that book too! We are two hearts that beat as one! I've got their breeches, and their soft slippers too, and can run as fast as the next man! I am grateful to you, brother, for giving me such good advice! I would have said the same to you, but I had not the courage. As for our master, if he is taken I doubt if he will escape from the hands of Pleberio's men. So he will not be able to reproach us afterwards for failing to protect him, or accuse us of running away!

SEMPRONIO. Ah, friend Parmeno, how happy and fruitful a thing is harmony between friends! Even if Celestina did nothing else for us she will have served her turn in bringing us together.

PARMENO. That is true and no one can deny it! Just because we were ashamed to speak up, and afraid of being accused of cowardice, we might have stayed here and died with our master. And he's the only one who deserves to die!

SEMPRONIO. Melibea must be there! Listen, someone is speaking!

PARMENO. I fear it may not be her, but someone imitating her voice!

SEMPRONIO. God save us from all traitors! I hope they are not guarding the road by which we must escape. That's what I am most afraid of.

CALISTO. This noise is made by more than one person. I will speak whatever comes of it. Hist, hist! My lady!

LUCRETIA. That is Calisto's voice. I will speak to him. Who is there? Who calls?

CALISTO. He who comes in obedience to your commands.

LUCRETIA. Why do you not come closer, lady? Approach without fear, for Calisto is come.

MELIBEA. Fool, speak more softly! Go and make sure it is Calisto!

LUCRETIA. Come, lady, it is certainly he. I recognize his voice.

CALISTO. I have been tricked! That is not Melibea's voice! I hear a noise! I am lost! But whether I live or die, I will not quit this place.

MELIBEA. Go, Lucretia, wait inside! Oh, sir, what is your name? Who told you to come here?

CALISTO. She who has the right to command the whole world, she whom I am unworthy to serve! Do not fear to make yourself known to one who is enslaved by your beauty, for the sweetness of your voice, which sounds ever in my ear, tells me truly you are my lady Melibea, and I am your slave Calisto.

MELIBEA. The strange audacity of your message has forced me to come and speak to you, lord Calisto! You know already how I have received your offers. What more do you want of me than the answer you have already had? Leave these vain and foolish thoughts, and let my honour and my person remain free from blame and slander. I have come here only to beg you to leave me and trouble me no more. Do not seek to put my reputation at the mercy of malicious tongues!

CALISTO. Nothing can shake the resolution of a heart forewarned against adversity. But alas, I am disarmed! Without fear of deceit or treachery I came here to-night secure in your love. Have I not then reason to lament if you prove obdurate, and bid me retrace in sorrow the path I trod with such sweet and pleasing anticipation? O unhappy Calisto! How you have been deceived by those who swore to serve you! O treacherous Celestina! Why did you not leave me to die? Why did you raise my hopes and feed the fire which devours me? Why did you falsely report the words of this lady whom I adore? Why have you sought to destroy me with your lying tongue? Why send me here expecting words of love, only to hear those lips which I adore speak harsh disdain, distrust, and hatred? O my enemy! Did you not tell me that my lady was favourably disposed towards me? Did you not say that it was her wish that I, her prisoner, should come here? Not to be driven away with scorn, but to hear the repeal of my former banishment? In whom can I trust? Where lies the truth? Who is without guile? Where shall I find a true friend, a frank enemy, a loyal servitor? Is there any place free from traitors? Who dared with false words lure me here to my destruction?

MELIBEA. My lord, cease your just complaints! My heart can no longer bear them, nor my eyes refrain from tears. You weep for despair and call me cruel! I weep for joy and call you faithful! O my lord and my all, how happy I should be if I could see your face as well as hear your voice! But since that is impossible take this affirmation and seal of the words I sent you written on the lips of our trusty messenger. All I said then I confirm, and think it good. Dry your tears, sir, and do with me what you will!

CALISTO. O my lady, hope of my glory, repose and alleviation of my pain, joy of my heart! No tongue could speak the thanks you deserve for the incomparable gift that at this joyous moment I receive from you! Will you permit this humble and despicable creature to enjoy that which I thought myself unworthy of, much as I desired it? Dare I hope for such felicity, remembering your noble birth, considering your perfections, contemplating your beauty, conscious of my worthlessness and your great merits, your wondrous graces and your many and manifold virtues? O great God, how can I praise Thee enough, since Thou hast performed for me so unexpected a miracle? Oh, how long I have lived in hopes of this moment and thrust the thought from my mind, considering it impossible! And now the bright beams of your clear beauty enlighten my eyes, enflame my heart, loosen my tongue, invigorate my thoughts, vanquish my timidity, increase my strength, set free my hands and feet! They gave me courage and strength, and drew me to this hallowed spot where now I find myself, listening to the heavenly strains of your sweet voice! And truly, if I had not heard and enjoyed it before this, I would never have believed that these honeyed words were not designed to cozen me! But though I am now sure of your sincerity, I still marvel that such happiness should be granted to me. Am I indeed Calisto?

MELIBEA. Lord Calisto, I was never for one moment insensible to your wondrous beauty, your great merit, your high birth! Since I first saw you you have been always in my thoughts. At first I fought to hide my love, but I could not do it. It was so strong that when Celestina first spoke your sweet name to me I could no longer conceal my passion. And so I have come here by night, in order that you may lay your commands on me and dispose of my person as you will. These doors bar your approach, and for that reason I curse their strong bolts and lament my puny strength! Were it otherwise you would have no cause to complain, and I should not languish here in sorrow!

CALISTO. Why, my lady, do you think I would allow a mere plank of wood to keep us apart? Nothing can separate us but your own will and resolution. O troublesome and importunate doors! God grant that you may perish in a fire like that which devours me! The least touch of it would shrivel you up in an instant! Now, in God's name, lady, let me call my servants and bid them hack these doors in pieces!

PARMENO. Do you hear that, Sempronio? Do you hear? He wants to involve us in this business. I do not like the way things are going. I am afraid this escapade of his will get us all into trouble. I'm off!

SEMPRONIO. Softly, wait a bit! She does not agree to it!

MELIBEA. Dear love, do you wish me to lose my good name and reputation? Do not be so impatient! Our hope is certain and time is too short now to do as you suggest. Ah, you feel your pain only, I that of us both! You weep for yourself alone, I for you and for myself! Be content to come to-morrow at this same hour to the orchard wall! If you break down these cruel doors now we may be discovered at

once. And if not, yet by to-morrow morning everyone in my
father's house will be the sharer of my guilty secret. And you
know 'the greater the sinner, the greater the sin!' So it will
immediately be known to the whole city!

SEMPRONIO. In an evil hour we came here to-night, and here
we shall have to stay, judging by the time our master is taking.
Fortune has favoured us so far, but we may yet be heard in
the house or by the neighbours.

PARMENO. For the last two hours I have been urging you to
come away so as to avoid the consequences of this unfortunate
affair!

CALISTO. O my lady and my life, why do you call that guilty
which has been conceded to me by the saints of God? I was
praying for this before the high altar when Celestina brought
me your kind message.

PARMENO. Oh, you rave, you rave, Calisto! On my life,
brother, he is no true Christian! It was the old whore with
her pestilential witchcraft who brought about this meeting,
and now he says it was the saints of God who arranged it for
him! And in this belief he wants to break down the doors.
And he will no sooner have struck the first blow than he will
be heard and captured by the servants of Melibea's father, who
are sleeping just beside us!

SEMPRONIO. Do not be afraid, Parmeno—we are standing far
enough away. If we hear a noise we have a good chance of
escape. Do not trouble about him! If he behaves foolishly
he alone must pay the penalty!

PARMENO. You say exactly what I was thinking! We will do
as you suggest, and avoid death, for we are too young to die!
It is not cowardice to fear to kill or be killed, but common
sense! Pleberio's men are fools, they are more anxious to
quarrel and fight than to eat and sleep! We should prove
ourselves even greater fools to provoke an enemy who loves
war and disorder more than victory and the glory of conquest.

Oh, if you could only see me now, brother, you would be proud of me! My body is already poised for flight, legs apart, the left foot forward! My coat-tails are tucked into my belt, and my shield is well under my arm so as not to get in my way. By God, I believe I could run like a deer, I am so frightened!

SEMPRONIO. I am even better prepared, for I have strapped my sword and buckler together so that I shall not drop them as I run, and I have put my helmet into the hood of my cloak.

PARMENO. But what have you done with the stones you had there?

SEMPRONIO. Thrown them out, so as to move more lightly, for I have enough to do to run at all in this cuirass which you so stupidly forced on me! I was very loth to put it on, for I guessed it would be too heavy to run in! Listen, listen, do you hear anything, Parmeno? Things are going badly! We are dead men! Run quickly, let us go to Celestina's house in case they try to cut us off from our own!

PARMENO. Hurry, hurry! How slow you are! Oh, miserable sinner that I am! If they seem about to catch us throw everything away, sword, buckler and all!

SEMPRONIO. Have they killed our master?

PARMENO. I don't know! I am not worried about him! I have other things to worry about!

SEMPRONIO. Stop, stop, Parmeno! Come back, come back, quietly! It is only the watch going noisily along the next street.

PARMENO. Are you sure? Do not trust to your eyes alone, for they often mistake one thing for another! Oh, they've not left me one drop of blood in my veins! I was already at grips with death, who seemed to be raining great blows on my back! By God, I was never so afraid in my life before, nor thought myself in such danger, though I have known hard times and been in some tight corners. For nine years I served in the monastery at Guadalupe, and I and my fellow servants came to blows a thousand times. But I was never in such a fear of death as now!

SEMPRONIO. And didn't I serve the priest of St Michael, the hotel-keeper in the market-place, and the gardener Mollejas? Never a day went by without a fight with the bird-scarers, who threw stones at the birds that perched on our great poplar-tree, to stop them raiding the garden! But God defend us from going armed, for that is the great danger! Do they not say: 'Laden with arms, laden with fear'? Come back, come back! It is only the watch, for sure!

MELIBEA. Lord Calisto, what is that noise in the street? It sounds like men running. For God's sake take care! You are in danger!

CALISTO. Lady, do not be afraid, I am in no danger. It must be my own men. They are brave fellows and will disarm all who pass. Someone is running away from them no doubt!

MELIBEA. Did you bring many men with you?

CALISTO. No, only two! But they are so courageous that they would easily disarm and put to flight half a dozen men between them. They are picked men, lady! I do not go ill attended. If I had not feared for your reputation I would have made them break down these doors. They would have done it easily. And if we had been overheard they would soon have saved us both from your father's men.

MELIBEA. Oh, sir, in God's name, do not attempt anything so rash! But I am glad you have such faithful followers. They earn well the bread they eat. Since nature has endowed them with such good qualities treat them well, sir, for my sake, and reward them richly, so that they will keep our secret. And when you are forced to correct their faults mix some kindness with your correction, so that their brave hearts are not too downcast and discouraged to be daring at the right time.

PARMENO. Hist, hist, sir! Make haste to be gone! Here

comes a crowd of people with torches. You will be seen and recognized, for there is nowhere to hide.

CALISTO. O wretched Calisto! Lady, I am constrained to take my leave of you! Believe me, I am not so much moved by fear of death as by respect for your good name. Since I must go good angels be your guard! I will come to the orchard to-morrow night at this time, as you commanded me.

MELIBEA. So be it! God go with you!

PLEBERIO. Lady wife, are you asleep?

ALISA. No, my lord!

PLEBERIO. Can you hear a noise in our daughter's room?

ALISA. Yes, I think I can. Melibea, Melibea!

PLEBERIO. She does not hear you. I will call louder. Daughter Melibea!

MELIBEA. Sir?

PLEBERIO. What footsteps are those I hear in your room?

MELIBEA. Sir, Lucretia's! I was thirsty and sent her to get me a drink of water.

PLEBERIO. Well, go to sleep again, daughter. I was sure it was someone else!

LUCRETIA. It doesn't take much to wake them! They were quite worried!

MELIBEA. There is no animal so gentle that it does not become fierce in defence of its young. What would they say if they knew I had been out of my room!

CALISTO. Shut the doors, boy; and you, Parmeno, take a light into my room.

SEMPRONIO. Sir, you should rest! It is almost day.

CALISTO. I will, for I have great need of repose. Well, Parmeno, what do you think now of the old woman you so scorned? See the results of her handiwork! What should I have done without her?

PARMENO. Sir, I did not realize how desperate you were, nor how gracious and how desirable Melibea was! So I am not to blame! I knew Celestina and her tricks, and so I advised you as I thought best, for you are my master. But now she seems to me quite different. She has completely changed!

CALISTO. How has she changed?

PARMENO. In such a way that if I had not seen it with my own eyes I would not have believed it! But it is as true as I live!

CALISTO. Tell me, did you hear what passed between myself and my lady? What were you doing? Were you afraid?

SEMPRONIO. Afraid, sir? What of? All the world could not make us afraid! You must look elsewhere for timorous men! We were there, waiting for you, all ready, our swords in our hands.

CALISTO. Did you sleep at all?

SEMPRONIO. Sleep, sir? Only boys sleep! I did not even sit down! I stood poised on my toes, looking all round me, so that if I heard anything I could act quickly, and do all that my strength would allow. Even Parmeno, though you may think he has not always served you with a very good grace, was as pleased when he saw people coming with torches as the wolf is when he scents the approaching flock! If there had not been so many of them he would have made short work of some!

CALISTO. That need not astonish you. It proceeds from his naturally warlike character. Even if he had not had me to defend, he would still have felt the same. Such men cannot go against their natures. Can the leopard change his spots? Truly, as I told my lady Melibea, I knew I was safe with you two to look after me. Lads, I am much beholden to you both! If it pleases God to keep me in good health, I will reward you as you deserve for your faithful service. Go now with God and sleep well!

PARMENO. Where shall we go, Sempronio? To our beds to sleep, or to the buttery to eat?

SEMPRONIO. You may go where you like, but for my part I am going straight to Celestina's to claim my share in her reward. She is a whoreson old hag, and I don't want to give her time to think up some excuse to cheat us of our rights.

PARMENO. Well said! I had forgotten about that. Let us both go, and if she tries to play any tricks on us we will give her such a fright that she will soon repent. There are no friendships in business!

SEMPRONIO. Softly now, not a word! She sleeps by this little window. Rat-tat, Mother Celestina, open up!

CELESTINA. Who calls?

SEMPRONIO. Open the door! It is your sons!

CELESTINA. None of my sons runs about the streets at this time of night!

SEMPRONIO. Open to Parmeno and Sempronio! We have come to have breakfast with you.

CELESTINA. Oh, you mad rogues! Come in, come in! How chances it that you come so early? It is only just getting light. What have you been doing? What has happened? Has Calisto failed in his enterprise or succeeded? How goes it?

SEMPRONIO. You may well ask! If it had not been for us he would be already in his grave and at peace for ever! If he valued our services at their true worth, all his wealth could not pay the debt. At least, so I suppose, if what they say is true, that life is our most precious possession!

CELESTINA. Jesu, Jesu! Tell me what happened, for God's sake?

SEMPRONIO. We were in terrible danger! My blood still runs cold to think of it.

CELESTINA. Calm yourself, in God's name, and tell me all about it.

PARMENO. You are asking too much of him. We are so worn and wearied by the fatigues of this night, you would do better to get us a meal first. Then perhaps we shall be able to tell you all our adventures. For I don't mind telling you that I am not in the humour to meet a peaceful man! My delight would be to meet someone on whom to vent my anger, for those who roused it ran so fast that we had no time to close with them.

CELESTINA. Pox take me if I am not afraid of you, you look so grim! But I think you are only joking! Tell me now, Sempronio, truly, what happened?

SEMPRONIO. By God, I am beside myself with rage! I am desperate! But I must calm down and not treat you as I would my enemy. I was never one to threaten the weak and oppress those who cannot defend themselves. Lady, all my weapons are broken, my shield without its rim, my sword hacked, my helmet squashed flat on my head! I have nothing left with which to defend my master, if need arises, and to-night he is to meet Melibea in her father's orchard. It is all agreed. But how can I buy new weapons? It will be no wonder if I am left for dead!

CELESTINA. You must ask your master to get you new weapons. They were lost in his service. You know he would do it at once. He is not one of those who say: 'Take service with me, but get your wages where you can!' He is so generous he will give you enough money to equip yourself afresh, and more beside!

SEMPRONIO. Ah, but Parmeno is in like case! So all my master has will go on new weapons. How can you think I should be so greedy as to ask for more when he has already dealt so generously with us? No one shall say of me that given an inch I take an ell! He gave us one hundred gold pieces! Then he gave us a gold chain! A third such gift would ruin him! This affair is likely to cost him dear enough. Let us be content with what we have, and not lose all like the dog in the fable, who lost the substance for the shadow through being too grasping.

CELESTINA. (He's amusing, this ass!) Upon my life, if we were at dinner I would say you were drunk! Are you in your right mind, Sempronio? What has your reward to do with mine, your wages with my just recompense? Am I obliged to pay for your weapons and supply all you lack? May I drop dead if you have not caught up a careless word I let fall the other day as we came along the street. I know I said that all I had was yours, that if you were in need I would do what little I could for you, and that if God let me prosper with your master you would not lose by it. But you know, Sempronio, that these little remarks, these polite phrases, mean nothing! All is not gold that glisters! If it were it would cost more! What do you say, Sempronio? I may be old, my son, but I still have wit enough to read what is in your mind! And now I will tell you truly, in good faith, I am in great trouble myself. I could die of disappointment! When I came back from your house I gave that feather-brain, Elicia, the little chain your master gave me to amuse herself with. And now she cannot remember what she has done with it! And all night neither she nor I has slept a wink. Not because of its value, for it was worth very little, but because of her stupidity and my chagrin. Some of my friends happened to come in just at that time, and I am afraid one of them may have taken it, on the principle of 'finding's keeping!' But before we go any further, lad, there is one point we must clear up. If your master gives me anything it's mine—you must allow that! I did not ask for a share in your satin doublet, nor will I! We all serve him and he gives to each what he deserves. If he has given me anything, well, I have twice risked my life for it! I have done more for him, and lost more in the doing, than either of you. You can well imagine, my sons, that all this business has been very expensive. And my wisdom did not come without pain and labour, as Parmeno's mother could well testify if she were here, God rest her soul! I have earned

my reward. You must look to him for yours. All this has
meant trouble and toil for me, pleasure and pastime for you!
You must not expect to be paid the same for enjoying yourselves as I for hard work! Nevertheless, in spite of what I
have said, if my chain is found I will give you each a pair of
scarlet breeches, for that is the apparel most suitable for young
men! If it is not, then you must take the will for the deed
and I alone will bear the loss. And this I do out of pure love,
and because it was through you that I, and not another, had
the handling of this affair. And if you are not content you
must take your complaints elsewhere!

SEMPRONIO. This is not the first time I have found avarice to
be the worst fault of old people! If they are poor they are
envious; if rich, miserly! So avarice increases with wealth,
and covetousness with poverty. Nothing makes the miser
so poor as wealth! O God, and how necessity grows with
abundance! This old woman told me to take all the profit
in this affair if I wanted it, thinking it would yield but little.
Now, seeing how much it is, she will give nothing away. And
so she proves the truth of the old saying: 'The more we have,
the more we want!'

PARMENO. Let her give us what she promised or we will take
it all! I told you what she was like, but you would not believe
me.

CELESTINA. If you are angry with yourselves, or with your
master, because you have lost your weapons, do not seek to
pick a quarrel with me! I know the reason for all this! I
know where the shoe pinches! It is not necessity which makes
you so rough with me, nor is it greed. You think you will
always have to be content with Elicia and Areusa, and that I
do not intend to procure other pleasures for you. Leave these
demands for money, stop these threats of violence, and be
patient! She who was able to bring these two women to your
beds can easily get you a dozen others, especially now that you

are more experienced, more sensible, and more deserving! Parmeno can tell you that I always keep my promises in matters of this kind! Speak up, Parmeno, don't be afraid to tell him what happened the other night!

SEMPRONIO. Let him unbutton his breeches if he likes! I have not come here for that! Do not try to make fools of us any longer, for on my life that cock won't fight! Stop trying to wheedle me! I am too old a dog to come to heel when you whistle. Give us two-thirds of what Calisto gave you. Do not drive us to take it all by force. Keep your flatteries for other greenhorns, you old whore!

CELESTINA. Have you forgotten who I am, Sempronio? Do you call me whore? Be quiet and do not insult my white hairs! I am an old woman as God made me, and none the worse for that! I live by my work, as other men do, and reasonably well too! I do not have to beg for employment. If people want my help they have to come and find me. If I live well or ill, God is my judge! And do not think you can threaten me, for the law is for all, and all are equal before it. Even though I am a woman they will listen to me and you will be punished. Leave me alone with what belongs to me! And do not think I am in your power, Parmeno, because you happen to know the secrets of my past life, and all that passed between me and your unhappy mother! She was wont to play these same tricks on me when it pleased her!

PARMENO. Do not remind me of that or I may be tempted to send you to carry your complaints to her in person!

CELESTINA. Elicia, Elicia! Get up, come here, and bring me my cloak! By all the saints in heaven, I will go and clamour like a madwoman before some justice of the peace! What is all this? Do you dare to threaten me in my own house? Are you trying out your courage and your valour on some tame old sheep or tethered hen? No, but on an old woman of seventy! Go to, vent your rage on men like yourselves, men who wear swords, not on my frail distaff! It is a great proof of cowardice to attack the weak and those who are powerless to resist. Filthy flies bite only the thin weak cattle; barking curs attack only poor passers-by! If she who lies in that bed had only listened to me, our house would not have been without a man to-night, our sleep would not have been so rudely disturbed. But to please you, Sempronio, to remain faithful to you, she decided to sleep alone. And because there are only two poor defenceless women here, you come thundering in and threaten us! You would not dare to do it if there were a man in the house, for, as they say: 'The strong man armed keepeth his castle!'

SEMPRONIO. Avaricious old hag, dying of thirst for gold! Can you not be content with a third part of the profit?

CELESTINA. A third part? Out of my house, both of you! Be off with you before I call the neighbours! Do not drive me too far! Take care you do not betray Calisto's secrets and your own!

SEMPRONIO. Cry out, complain as much as you like! You will keep your promise or I will kill you here and now!

ELICIA. For God's sake put up your sword. Hold him, hold him, Parmeno! Don't let the madman kill her!

CELESTINA. Justice, justice, neighbours, justice! These ruffians will kill me in my own house!

SEMPRONIO. Ruffians? Where? Wait, you old witch, till I send you to complain in hell!

CELESTINA. Oh, he has killed me! Ah, ah, a priest, for the love of God!

PARMENO. Kill her, kill her! Finish off what you have begun or we shall be discovered! Let her die, let her die! And so perish all our enemies!

CELESTINA. For the love of God, a priest!

ELICIA. Oh, cruel men! Damnation to you and all your works! You have killed my mother, and with her all my hopes of happiness!

SEMPRONIO. Run, Parmeno, run, there's a crowd coming!
Look out, here comes the watch!

PARMENO. Death and destruction! There's no way of escape!
They have barred the door!

SEMPRONIO. I will jump out of the window rather than fall
into the hands of justice!

PARMENO. Jump, and I will follow you!

ACT THIRTEEN

SUMMARY: *Calisto wakes up and talks to himself. After a while he calls Tristan and his other servants. Then he falls asleep again. Tristan is standing by the door when Sosia arrives in tears. Questioned by Tristan, Sosia tells him of the deaths of Sempronio and Parmeno. They go and break the news to Calisto, who is greatly distressed.*

CALISTO.   Oh, how well I have slept since that brief moment of bliss, that happy meeting!   I have indeed rested well, calm and contented in my great joy!   Such deep sleep comes from bodily fatigue and from the relief and succour of my soul's anguish.   I am not surprised that they should combine to seal my eyes in slumber.   Last night my body was exercised in every limb, while my heart was thrilled to the uttermost by desire and fulfilment.   Truly they say sorrow breeds melancholy and melancholy hinders sleep!   So it was with me while I suffered for lack of that great joy I now possess!   O Melibea, my lady and my love!   What are you thinking of at this moment?   Are you asleep or awake?   Do you think of me or of another?   Are you up or still in bed?   Oh, happy and most fortunate Calisto, if it is true and not all a dream!   Did I dream it or not?   Was it a fantasy or did it really happen?   I was not alone, however!   My servants were with me—two of them.   If they say it happened I can believe it without hesitation.   I will send for them to confirm my joy.   Tristan, boy, Tristan, I say!   Get up and come here!

TRISTAN.   Sir, I am here already.

CALISTO. Run, fetch Sempronio and Parmeno!

TRISTAN. I go, sir!

CALISTO. Sleep, sad heart, be at rest,
    Suffer no more!
Melibea, divinely fair,
    Whom you adore,
Loves you, and with a kiss
    Banished your pain!
Cease to lament, be still,
    And sleep again!

TRISTAN. Sir, there is not a servant in the house!

CALISTO. Open the shutters!   See what time it is!

TRISTAN. Sir, it is broad daylight.

CALISTO. Well, close them again and leave me to sleep until it be time to eat.

TRISTAN. I will stand guard at the door, so that no one can disturb my master's slumbers.   I will refuse to let anyone in. But what is all that shouting in the market-place?   What can it be?   Is there an execution or has the bullfight begun already?   I cannot imagine what else it can be.   But here comes Sosia, my master's groom.   He will tell me what it is all about!   How dishevelled the wretched boy is!   He must have been tumbling in some tavern!   He will be severely whipped if my master sees him in that state!   He's a wild lad, but time will tame him no doubt!   But he seems to be in trouble!   He's in tears!   What is the matter, Sosia, why are you crying?   Where have you been?

SOSIA. Oh, Tristan, I am in great distress!   What a terrible loss!   My master's house is shamed for ever!   Oh, what a dreadful thing!   O unhappy young men!

TRISTAN. But what is the matter?   What has happened? Why are you wringing your hands?   What misfortune has overtaken us?

SOSIA. Sempronio and Parmeno——

TRISTAN. What of them? What is it, fool? Tell me quickly what has happened! You alarm me!

SOSIA. Our companions, our brothers——

TRISTAN. Either you are drunk or mad, or you bring bad news! Will you tell me plainly what has happened to Sempronio and Parmeno?

SOSIA. They lie beheaded in the market-place!

TRISTAN. Oh, a black day for us, truly, if this news be true! Did you see them, speak to them?

SOSIA. They were already almost dead. But one of them, seeing me watching with tears running down my face, raised his eyes to mine, and with a great effort lifted his hands to heaven, as if imploring God's mercy, and begging me to bring back news of his death. Then, weeping, he bent his head in a sad farewell, as if to say that we should never meet again until the day of judgment.

TRISTAN. No, no, you misunderstood him! He was begging you to fetch Calisto. And if what you say is true we must go and tell him the sad news.

SOSIA. My lord, my lord!

CALISTO. What is it, wretch? Did I not forbid you to waken me?

SOSIA. Sir, wake up, rise, for if you do not succour us we are all dead men! Sempronio and Parmeno lie beheaded in the market-place like public malefactors, while the town crier blazons forth their misdeeds!

CALISTO. God help me, what is it you say? I cannot believe such terrible and unexpected news! Did you see them?

SOSIA. I saw them.

CALISTO. Be careful! Think what you are saying! They were with me all night.

SOSIA. And early this morning they died!

CALISTO. O my loyal servants! My faithful followers! O my discreet companions and counsellors! Can this be true?

O unhappy Calisto! You are shamed for ever! What will become of you, lacking two such loving friends? For God's sake, Sosia, tell me, why were they put to death? What did the town crier say? Where were they executed? Who gave the order?

SOSIA. Sir, the reason for their death was proclaimed by the town crier, who shouted out: 'Justice demands that the murderers should die!'

CALISTO. But whom could they have murdered so suddenly? What does this mean? It is not four hours since they left me! Do you know the name of the man they murdered?

SOSIA. Sir, it was a woman, one Celestina.

CALISTO. What!

SOSIA. So I was told.

CALISTO. If this is true kill me quickly! I will forgive you! This is far worse than you think! Are you sure they murdered Celestina, the old woman with the scarred face?

SOSIA. That's the one! I saw her lying in her house, pierced through with more than thirty sword-thrusts, and wept over by a young maidservant.

CALISTO. O miserable youths! How did they die? Did you see them, speak to them?

SOSIA. Oh, sir, if you had seen them it would have broken your heart! One had his brains knocked out and lay lifeless. The other had both his arms broken and his face smashed in. Both were covered in blood. They jumped out of a window high above the ground to escape the watch. They were practically dead men before their heads were cut off. I do not think they felt anything.

CALISTO. But I feel it, to my shame and disgrace! Would to God I had been there with them and lost my life rather than my honour and all hope of success in the enterprise I have undertaken! That is what grieves me most! O my poor name and reputation, how you will be bandied about in the market-place, my innermost secrets publicly proclaimed in the streets and shops of the city! What will become of me? Where can I hide? What will happen next? I cannot bring the dead to life again! Shall I stay here? That would look like cowardice! Whose advice can I ask? Tell me, Sosia, why did they murder her?

SOSIA. Sir, one of her servants, the one who was weeping by the body, cried out before everyone that it was because she would not share with them the gold chain you gave her.

CALISTO. O unhappy day, cruel tribulation! My gifts go from hand to hand and my name is on everyone's lips! Everything will be discovered, all my dealings with her and with them, and what they knew of my affairs, the business they had in hand for me! I shall not dare to show my face! O unhappy young men, how suddenly you met with disaster! O my joy, how are you departed! Well says the old proverb: 'The higher we climb the harder we fall!' All I gained last night I have lost this morning! There is no lull in a storm! I was well on my way to happiness if my good fortune could have calmed the winds that now blow me to destruction! O fortune, how often and on how many sides have you attacked me! Yet the more you dogged my footsteps and threatened my happiness, the more I sought to bear your blows with fortitude. For they show whether the heart be firm or feeble. There is no better proof of a man's strength and courage. Therefore, whatever evil or danger lies in wait for me, I will not fail to obey the orders of Melibea, for whose sake all this has happened. For the possession of all I hope for means more to me than the loss of those that are dead. They were reckless and foolhardy—they had to pay the penalty for it some time. The old woman was evil and false, as it well appears by her behaviour to them. So they quarrelled over the division of the spoil? God let her perish as a punishment for the evils she had done. I will order Sosia and Tristan to get ready.

They must set forth with me on the way I long to tread. They must bring ladders, for the orchard walls are high. To-morrow I will pretend that I have but just now returned from a journey. I will avenge my men's deaths if I can; if not I will make everyone believe I am innocent by saying I was not here. Or I will pretend to be mad, so that I may continue to enjoy the sweet fruits of love, as Ulysses did in order to escape the Trojan war and stay with his wife Penelope.

ACT FOURTEEN

SUMMARY: *Melibea is talking to Lucretia. She is distressed because Calisto, who had promised to visit her that night, has not yet arrived. But he keeps his promise, and comes with Sosia and Tristan. After he has had what he came for they all go home. Calisto shuts himself up in his room, lamenting how short a time he was able to spend with Melibea, and begging Phoebus to veil his light so that he may again enjoy her love.*

MELIBEA. The gentleman we are waiting for is very late! What do you think has delayed him, Lucretia?

LUCRETIA. Lady, I think there must be some good reason for his unpunctuality. Perhaps it was not in his power to come sooner!

MELIBEA. The blessed angels keep him from all harm and bring him to me quickly! Alas, I cannot help thinking of all the dangers that might beset him between his house and mine! Perhaps he decided to come to our meeting in disguise, as young men like to do at such times; and perhaps he met the watch, and they, not recognizing him, stopped him; and in defending himself he may have hurt one of them or been hurt himself! Or perhaps one of the watch-dogs, who are no respecters of persons, and make no difference between the intruder and the welcome guest, has bitten him to the bone! Or he may have fallen into the gutter, or into a ditch, and hurt himself! O unhappy Melibea! How many obstacles my love conjures up, that my imagination magnifies beyond all reason! God grant they may none of them be true! But

158

listen, listen! Footsteps sound in the street, and I think I hear voices on the other side of the wall.

SOSIA. Put the ladder here, Tristan! It is the best place, though rather high.

TRISTAN. Mount, sir! I will come with you, for we do not know who may be there. I hear voices.

CALISTO. Stay there, stupid creature! I will go alone. It is my lady's voice I hear.

MELIBEA. It is your servant, it is your slave, it is she who loves you better than herself! Oh, my lord, do not jump from so great a height! I shall die of fright! Come down slowly by the ladder! Do not be in such a hurry!

CALISTO. O angelic creature! Precious jewel, more lovely than any in the world! O my lady and my life, do I at last hold you in my arms? I cannot believe it. I have so longed to possess you that my joy is almost greater than I can bear!

MELIBEA. My lord, I have given myself into your hands! Do with me as you will! But do not make me pay more dearly for my submission than if I had been haughty and pitiless! Do not seek to ruin me for the gratification of an idle whim! Once we have done wrong it is easier to repent than to undo the wrong done. Be satisfied with what satisfies me, that is, to see you and know that you are here with me. Do not force me to yield that which can never be given back! Take heed, sir, how you destroy the treasure which nothing in the world can replace!

CALISTO. Lady, I have risked my life to obtain my reward. I should be foolish to refuse it when it is within my grasp. Surely you do not wish me to do that? Nor would I consent to it! Do not ask me to behave in such a faint-hearted way! It is more than any man could do, particularly if he loved as I do! All my life I have been straining towards this goal. You cannot be so cruel as to wish me to cease my pursuit at the very moment I hope to claim the sweet recompense of all my pain?

MELIBEA. Sir, let me entreat you! Let your tongue run on as it will, but keep your hands from wandering! Calm yourself! Be content to know that I am yours, and enjoy the outward form, which is the perfect bliss of all true lovers! Do not try to steal from me the greatest gift that nature has bestowed upon me! Take care! The good shepherd shears his sheep, and profits by it, but does not destroy them utterly!

CALISTO. Why all this hesitation, lady? Do you not wish to satisfy me? Must I continue to suffer? Must I return to the miseries of my former state? Lady, forgive my impatient hands! Once they would have thought themselves unworthy to touch your garments, but now they delight in the feel of your lovely body and your sweet and delicate flesh!

MELIBEA. Lucretia, go a little apart!

CALISTO. Why, madam? I am glad that she should witness the consummation of my joy!

MELIBEA. I do not wish her to see my folly! If I had thought you would behave so unkindly to me I would not have trusted my person to your cruel conversation!

SOSIA. Tristan, do you hear that? I think things are going well!

TRISTAN. So well, indeed, that I hold my master to be the luckiest man in the world! Yet, to tell you the truth, although I am but a boy I think I could acquit myself as well!

SOSIA. Any man would be glad to steal such a treasure. But he is wise to enjoy her while he can, for she has cost him dear! Two men's lives went to the making of this love feast!

TRISTAN. He has already forgotten that! You can die in the service of such heartless brutes and they will not lift a finger to save you! You would be a fool to expect them to! When I first went into service with the count my mother warned me never to kill a man. See how happy they are in their embraces, while those who served them lie shamefully beheaded!

MELIBEA. O my lord and my life! How could you be so

cruel as to ravish me of my crown of virtue, my glorious
virginity, for a brief moment's pleasure so quickly over? O
my poor mother! If you knew what had happened would
you not pray for death, or even kill me in your anger? You
would not hesitate to become the executioner of your own
child, and I should be the unhappy cause of your death! O
my most honoured father! How have I sullied your reputation and given you cause for weeping and lamentation! Oh,
traitor that I am! Oh, my lord, why did I not foresee the
dangers that would result from your secret visits and the perils
that would menace me?

SOSIA.   She should have thought of all that before! They all
carry on like this when the damage is done! And that fool
Calisto takes her seriously!

CALISTO.   Day breaks already! How can that be? It seems
to me that we have only spent an hour together, and yet the
clock strikes three!

MELIBEA.   For God's sake, since I am wholly yours, since you
are my lord and my master, and I can no longer deny my love
for you, do not stay away from me too long! Come secretly
by night, as soon as you can, to this place at the same hour,
and I will wait for you here, so that we can again enjoy each
other's love! For the moment, God speed you! You will
not be seen, for it is still dark, and I shall not be heard in the
house, for it is not yet day.

CALISTO.   Boy, put up the ladder!

SOSIA.   Sir, here it is, you may come down!

MELIBEA.   Lucretia, come here! I am all alone—my lord has
gone! He has left his heart with me and taken mine in
exchange! Did you hear anything?

LUCRETIA.   No, madam, I slept all the time.

SOSIA.   Tristan, we must go quietly, for this is the hour when
rich men rise, the covetous count their gains, the pious go to
church, young lovers, like my master, run home, workers are

abroad in the fields, the labourers and those shepherds who take their folded sheep to the milking-sheds! And one among them, passing by, might happen to overhear a remark which would defame the honour of Melibea.

TRISTAN. Oh, fool, fit only to tend on horses! You say we must be silent and then speak her name! You'd make a fine captain to guide men by night through Moorish territory! Saying something must not be said, you say it; in seeking to hide it, you reveal it; to save it, you attack it; to impose silence, you chatter and call out! You ask questions and answer them yourself! Since you are so clever, perhaps you can tell me the month of the feast of St Mary in August! Then we shall know if there is enough hay in the house to feed you this year!

CALISTO. My worries are quite different from yours! Come in quietly, so as not to be heard in the house! Shut the door and let us all go to bed. I will go alone to my chamber and disarm, and you go to your rooms! Ah, strange creature that I am, how agreeable to me is solitude and silence and obscurity! I do not know whether it is from grief at my treason, in leaving my lady before it was full daylight, or from sorrow at my shame! Why, what is this? I feel the wound now that it is cold. Now that the blood runs sluggishly which yesterday leapt in my veins, I perceive the stain on my honour, the gap in my household, the loss of my fortune, the infamy which will fall on me as the result of my servants' execution! What have I done? What false step have I taken? Why did I not rise up at once like a man unjustly accused, the swift and savage avenger of the manifest wrong done to me? O miserable sweetness of this most transient life! What is there about you so enviable that a man would not rather die at once than linger on, infamous and dishonoured, his shame outweighing the good reputation built up over many years, uncertain at what instant the end will come? We are time's debtors and must pay all at once! Why did I not go out immediately to discover the true cause of my manifest perdition? O fleeting pleasures of this world! How brief their glory is, how much it costs! Repentance is not so dearly bought! Unhappy man, how shall I bear so great a loss? What shall I do? Where turn for good advice? To whom confide my shame? Why have I hidden it from my household and my family? 'I have been tried and found wanting, and no one in my household knows it!' I must act at once! But it is too late to confess I was there, too soon to deny it! I need time to seek out my friends, my former retainers, my parents, my allies, to arm myself, to set in motion the act of vengeance! O cruel judge! How have you repaid the bread eaten at my father's table? I thought that, secure in your support, I could kill a thousand men without fear of retribution! Iniquitous traitor, perverter of the truth, low-born hireling! Well may they say that you were appointed judge for lack of a better man! You might have remembered that you and those you condemned to death were once fellow servants to me and to my family! But when the vile man grows rich he remembers neither friends nor family. Who would have thought you would so utterly destroy me? Surely there is nothing worse than an unknown enemy! It is an old saying: 'From the forest he brought the wood that consumes him' and 'I reared the crow that now picks out my eye!' You whose sins are known to all the world have condemned to death those guilty of only a private error. But know that such private sins are less reprehensible than those committed publicly, less blamable, according to the laws of Athens! And those laws are not written in blood, for they say that it is better to pardon the criminal than to risk punishing the innocent. Oh, how difficult it is to uphold a righteous cause before unrighteous judges! How much more difficult then for my poor servants, who were not altogether blameless? Remember, if you have done evil, that there are judges in heaven and on earth! God and the king will call you criminal, and I a mortal enemy! But if one sinned, why kill the other, only for having been in his company? But what am I saying? To whom do I speak this? Am I in my right mind? Why, Calisto, do you dream? The man you accuse is not here! Whom do you quarrel with? Come to your senses! Remember the absent are always in the wrong! You must hear both sides of the question before you pronounce judgment. Do you not know that to execute justice one must forget friendship, kinship, even gratitude? Do not forget that all are equal before the law! Romulus, the founder of Rome, condemned his own brother to death because he had offended against the law. The Roman Torquatus killed his own son because he disobeyed the orders of the tribunes. Many others have done as much! Consider that if that judge were here, he would say that doing and consenting to the deed merit the same punishment; and so he ordered both to be executed, though only one had sinned. And if he hastened their death it was because their crime was notorious and did not need to be proved, for they were taken red-handed in the act of murder. One was already at the point of death from the effects of his fall. I believe the judge was alarmed by the clamour of Celestina's maid, that young girl she kept in her house, and so, to prevent confusion, to lessen my disgrace, to avoid waiting until the neighbours came running at her cries, which would have brought even greater shame on me, he did justice on them so early in the morning. And for justice to be done it needed the public executioner and the town crier. For all that I now believe I ought to be grateful to him for the rest of my life! For he has acted like a true friend, and not as a mere hanger-on of my father's household. And even if I am wrong, even if everything was not done for the best, remember, Calisto, the great joy of this past night! Remember your lady and the great happiness you knew with her! And since you hold your life dear only for her sake, what matters to you the death of any other man? No suffering can equal the ecstasy you have known. O my lady and my life, how much I offend you by forgetting you for one moment! How little I seem to value the great gift you have given me! I will not fall a prey to melancholy thoughts, I will not make a friend of grief! O incomparable gift! O ineffable satisfaction! What further reward can I ask of God, if indeed I deserve any reward, in this life? Why am I not satisfied? I must not be ungrateful to her who has already given me so much. I must show her how I value her gift, and not let myself be so overwhelmed with sorrow that I fail to enjoy my bliss to the full. I do not ask for any other honour or glory than this; no other riches, no other father or mother, no other friends or kindred. I will stay in my room all day, and at night I will take my pleasure in that sweet paradise, that delightful orchard, among the sweet-smelling flowers and fresh greenery. O happy night, would you were here! Bright Phoebus, hasten on your way! Shining stars, appear before your wonted time! O tardy clock, could I but see you burn with the fierce flame of love! If the stroke of midnight were to bring you the joys I anticipate, you would never submit to the will of the master who made you! And you, wintry months that lie yet in the womb of time, come soon with your long nights to take the place of these endless summer days! It seems a year already since last I saw that blessed place, that happy refuge from all my sufferings! But what am I asking? What am I so foolishly demanding with such impatience? That which has never been, and never can be! I cannot change the course of nature, for all is immutably fixed. Life and death move to an unalterable rhythm. Bounds are set to the secret movements of the high celestial firmament, of the planets, and of the North Star, to the monthly waxing and waning of the moon. Sea, fire, air, heat, cold, all are subject to the same laws. What

M 100

would it profit me if my clock struck twelve, if the heaven's
did not also? However early I rise day dawns no sooner!
But O my imagination, with whom nothing is impossible,
come to my aid! Evoke before my eyes the sweet presence of
my dear love! Let her gentle voice sound ever in my ears!
Let me hear again the broken phrases that fell from her rosy
lips: 'Leave me . . . do not approach . . . do not use me ill';
that faltering 'Do not seek to ruin me!' Let me remember
the loving embraces between each word, the way she repelled
and then drew me on, the way she fled only to return, her
honey-sweet kisses, the last farewell with which she took leave
of me. How much it cost her to pronounce the words! How
much despair, how many tears, which in spite of herself fell
like pearls from her bright shining eyes!

SOSIA. Tristan, what ought we to do about our master? He
has slept a long while. It is already four o'clock in the after-
noon, and he has not sent for us, nor has he had anything
to eat!

TRISTAN. Leave him alone! Sleep will do him good. He
is torn between sorrow for the death of his servants and
joy for the pleasure he has had with Melibea. Worn out
with two such conflicting emotions, what should he do but
sleep?

SOSIA. Do you think he wastes much time grieving over the
death of his two men? I think the young woman I see
through the window, passing along the street, grieves more
than he, or she would not wear a veil of that colour!

TRISTAN. Who is it, brother?

SOSIA. Come over here! You will catch a glimpse of her
before she disappears. Do you see that girl in black, wiping
the tears from her eyes? That is Elicia, maidservant to
Celestina and friend of Sempronio. A very pretty woman!
But she is a lost soul now, poor thing, for Celestina was a
mother to her and Sempronio her chief lover. In the house

she has just gone into lives a beautiful young woman, a fresh, joyous creature, very liberal in love, and much sought after, a famous whore who is only for those who can afford to pay her prices! Her name is Areusa. I know the unfortunate Parmeno passed many a sleepless night for love of her. His death will be a great blow to her.

ACT FIFTEEN

SUMMARY: *Areusa is engaged in an altercation with a ruffian named Centurio, who goes away when he hears Elicia coming. Elicia tells Areusa of the deaths caused by the love of Calisto and Melibea. They agree that Centurio must take vengeance on the lovers for the loss of their three friends. Finally Elicia leaves Areusa, without agreeing to her suggestion that they should set up house together, as she does not wish to give up her former pleasures, and prefers to remain in her old home.*

ELICIA. What can be the reason for all this clamour in my cousin's house? If she has already heard the news I bring, I shall miss the first outpourings of her grief, the sad reward of such a messenger. Weep, weep, let your tears overflow! Such men are not to be picked up at every street corner! I am glad she feels her loss. Let her tear her hair, as I have done in my despair! Let her learn that to lose such good friends is worse than death itself. Oh, I love her more than I thought possible for such a display of grief.

AREUSA. Out of my house, you villain, you swindler, you liar, you cheat! You must think me a fool to try and deceive me with such vain protestations! Thanks to your boasting and wheedling you have robbed me of all I possess! Vile creature! I have given you a cloak and a doublet, a sword and a buckler, shirts—two at a time—and a thousand other things, all of good quality. I have given you arms and a horse, and got you a place with a good master, whose shoes you are not worthy to untie. And now, when I ask you to do something for me, you find a thousand reasons to refuse!

CENTURIO.   Sister, ask me to kill ten men in your service, but not to go a mile on foot!

AREUSA.   Then why did you gamble away your horse, you worthless wretch? If it were not for me you would have been hanged long ago. Three times have I saved you from the gallows, four times paid your gambling debts. Why did I do it? I must be mad! Why do I remain faithful to this numskull? Why do I believe his lies and let him come into my house? What is he good for, with his matted hair and his scarred face? Twice he's been whipped, his sword-arm is useless, he keeps thirty whores in the stews! Get out of here! I never want to see you again! Don't speak to me, don't tell anyone you even know me! Otherwise, by the bones of the father that begot me and the mother that gave me birth, I will see you get a thousand blows on those bent shoulders of yours! You know I have friends who will do the job well!

CENTURIO.   Foul-mouthed hag! You must be mad! If I lose my temper someone will pay dearly for it! But I'll go now with no more ado! Someone is coming and we may be overheard.

ELICIA.   I may as well go in.   There are no lamentations here, only threats and angry words.

AREUSA.   O unhappy fool that I am! Is that you, my Elicia? Jesu, Jesu, can I believe my eyes? What's the matter? What grief are you hiding from me? What means this black cloak and this mourning veil? Truly you alarm me, sister! Tell me at once, what has happened? I have no idea what it can be, but the blood freezes in my veins already!

ELICIA.   Calamitous grief and bitter loss! I cannot speak one quarter of the sorrow I feel! These mourning garments cannot convey the despair of my heart and my entrails! O sister, sister, I can scarcely speak of it! The words stick in my throat.

AREUSA.   O unfortunate girl, you frighten me! Do not

keep me any longer in suspense, but tell me at once what has happened. Stop tearing your hair, wringing your hands, and beating your bosom! Does this grief touch us both? Does it concern me too?

ELICIA. O my dear cousin, my loving friend, Sempronio and Parmeno are no more! They are no longer in this world! Their souls have gone to answer for their sins! Their bodies are free of this sad life!

AREUSA. What are you trying to tell me? No more, for God's sake, or I shall die of grief!

ELICIA. There is yet worse to come, worse than you can ever imagine! Listen, and I will tell you my fatal news! Celestina, our friend and our mother, who fed me, sheltered me, made me the equal of anyone, famous throughout the city and far beyond, has gone to her last account! A thousand wounds I saw inflicted on her before my very eyes! She died in my arms!

AREUSA. O grief beyond compare! Sad news indeed, worthy of bitterest tears! O unexpected disaster, irreparable loss! How swiftly the wheel of fortune has turned! Who killed them? How did they die? I am amazed, overcome, like one who cannot believe her own ears. It is not a week since I saw them all in good health, and now we can only say 'God pardon them!' Tell me, dear sister, how did this cruel disaster come about?

ELICIA. I will tell you! You have heard, sister, of Calisto's love for that whey-faced Melibea? You know that Celestina, at Sempronio's suggestion, had agreed to act as go-between? She was to be well paid for her trouble. She went to work with such diligence and dispatch that she didn't have to knock twice! When Calisto found she had succeeded so quickly in a thing he thought impossible, he gave my poor aunt, among other things, a golden chain. And as it is only too true of this metal that it increases covetousness, so that the more we have of it the more we want, when she saw herself so rich she

ran off with her booty and refused to divide it with Sempronio
and Parmeno, though it had been agreed among them before-
hand that they should share whatever Calisto gave them.   One
morning, as they were coming home tired after staying out all
night in attendance on their master, and angered by some brawl
in which, they said, they had been involved, they came to ask
Celestina for their share of the gold chain, with which to make
good their losses.   But she refused to give them anything,
denied their pact, and swore she would keep for herself anything that was given to her.   Then she lost her temper and
let out a few secrets!   For, as they say, 'the angry tongue
cannot keep counsel!'   They disputed on both sides, she from
covetousness and love of gold, which always destroys friendship, they from fatigue and irritation because they had been
disappointed, which always sours our nature.   When they saw
she was not going to keep her promise they were beside themselves with rage.   They shouted and swore, and finally, finding
her adamant, they drew their swords and ran her through a
thousand times!

AREUSA.   O unhappy woman!   To think that she should come
to that in her old age!   And what about them?   How came
they to die?

ELICIA.   After they had committed their crime they tried to
escape from the watch, who happened to be passing.   They
jumped out of the window, were taken up almost dead, and
were beheaded immediately.

AREUSA.   O Parmeno, my love, how much reason I have to
lament your death!   How short a time we had to enjoy our
love!   But it could not last!   Now that this terrible thing has
happened, now that they are all dead and gone, and all our
tears cannot bring them back to life, do not grieve, good sister!
Do not blind yourself with weeping!   I do not think you have
lost more than I, and yet see how patiently I bear all this!

ELICIA.   Oh, I rage!   Unhappy that I am I shall go mad!

No one can feel it as I do!   No one has lost as much as I!
How much more plentiful and easy my tears would be for
another's loss than for my own!   What will become of me?
I have lost my mother, my haven, my refuge.   I have lost my
lover, who was almost a husband to me.   O good old Celestina, honourable and respected old woman!   How many
errors you saved me from by your good counsel!   You worked
while I enjoyed myself!   You went out, I stayed at home; you
went in rags, I in silken dresses; you came in laden like the
honey bee, while I wasted our substance, for I knew no better!
O joys and pleasures of this world, how little we esteem you
while we have you, and how much more we realize your value
when you are gone for ever!   O Calisto and Melibea, cause
of all these deaths, a curse light on your love!   May all your
pleasure turn to pain, your joy to travail, your laughter to
lamentation!   May the fresh grass on which you sport turn
to serpents and all your songs to groans!   May the shady
trees of the garden wither away before your eyes and the
sweet-scented flowers turn black.

AREUSA.   Softly, for pity's sake, sister, cease your threats!
Dry your tears!   Come, wipe your eyes and return to life,
for when one door shuts another opens!   Your grief is great,
but it will pass.   There are many ills which cannot be remedied,
but they can be avenged.   Your grief is beyond remedy, but
vengeance is easy.

ELICIA.   How can we be revenged?   By this threefold calamity
we are left friendless and alone.   I am as much concerned
with the punishment of the crime as with the crime itself.   But
what can I do?   All the worry of it falls on me.   Would to
God that I were with them and had no cause to weep their
deaths!   But what grieves me most is that in spite of what has
happened, that heartless man continues to enjoy his filthy
Melibea, while she is puffed up with pride to see blood shed
for her sake!

AREUSA. If that is so, then on whom can we more fittingly
take revenge? They have had their pleasure, now they must
pay for it. Leave it all to me! I will soon find out all about
them, where they meet, and when, for how long, and at what
time. If I do not embitter their love, never believe me to be
the old pastry-woman's daughter, as you know well I am!
And for this affair I will employ the man with whom I was
arguing when you came in. If he does not prove a worse
enemy to Calisto than Sempronio to Celestina, never trust me
more! How happy he will be if I ask him to do this for me!
For he was very cast down by my angry words. He will see
the heavens open when I take him back into favour and send
him about my business! But tell me, sister, how I can find
out what is happening in this affair? For I will devise a trap
to make Melibea weep as much as she now rejoices!

ELICIA. Friend, I know one of Parmeno's companions, a
groom called Sosia, who goes every night to Melibea's house
with Calisto. I think I can get all his secrets out of him, and
that will be enough to begin with.

AREUSA. No, I think it would be better if you sent Sosia here
to me. I will cajole him and wheedle him with a thousand
flatteries, until there is nothing left to discover, and then I will
make him and his master pay for their pleasures! And
Elicia, my dear soul, do not grieve any longer! Bring your
clothes and your furniture here, and come and keep me company. You mustn't stay alone, for sorrow is the friend of
solitude. A new love will help you to forget the old ones. A
new-born son makes up for three that have died! With a new
lover you can revive the happy memories and sweet pleasures
of former days. You shall share all I have. I grieve more
over your distress than over those who are gone. How true
it is that when we lose what we have enjoyed, our pain is
greater than the pleasure we take in hoping for things to come!
But the evil is without remedy. The dead cannot return, and,

as they say, 'they are dead, we live!' And, believe me, I will look after the living! I will make them drink the bitter cup they have prepared for you. Oh, cousin, when I am angry I know how to mix such a draught, though I am but young! And may God deal with all my enemies as Centurio shall deal with Calisto!

ELICIA. But be careful! I am afraid that even if I send Sosia to you it will not have the result you anticipate. The death of those who were punished for letting out this secret will make the survivors more zealous to keep it! I am grateful to you for offering me a home. God keep you and give you all you ask for! You have proved that your kinship and goodwill are not mere empty words, and that in need you are a friend indeed! But though I would like to come and enjoy the pleasure of your company, I fear it would do me too much harm. I need not explain to you what I mean, for I speak to one who well understands such matters! I am well known, sister, in my present quarters. I am among friends. The house will always be known as Celestina's house, God rest her soul! All the lively young girls who know it well, and who are my friends and companions, will continue to call there. They will meet their lovers there and I shall get a little profit from that. The few friends I have left might not follow me to another house. You know how hard it is to alter one's habits, and changes may be dangerous. A rolling stone gathers no moss! Besides, the rent of the house is paid for the year and I do not want to forfeit it. And although it is not much every little helps! Now I think it is time for me to go. I will not forget my promise. God be with you! I am on my way!

ACT SIXTEEN

SUMMARY: *Pleberio and Alisa, thinking their daughter Melibea to be still a virgin, which, as we have seen, is not the case, talk of her marriage. She overhears their conversation, and is so distressed by it that she sends Lucretia to interrupt them, and so force them to change the subject.*

PLEBERIO. Alisa, good wife, it seems to me that time, as they say, is slipping between our fingers! The days run on like the waters of the river. Nothing is so swiftly over as this life of ours. Death is ever at our heels; we are near neighbours to him, and soon must lie down under his banner, as nature decrees. This we perceive most clearly if we look round at our contemporaries, our brothers and our near relations. They all go to their eternal rest, the earth swallows them all up! And since we do not know when it may be our turn, though we know by positive signs that it must come, we should gird up our loins and prepare ourselves for this enforced march. Then cruel death, when he comes, will not come unexpectedly. We must get ready while we have time, for it is best to be prepared, and not taken by surprise. We must look for a son-in-law to inherit our estate, and give our only daughter a husband such as our position entitles her to. Then we can go tranquilly and without regret out of this world. I think the time has come to settle this matter. We have often discussed it, but now we must put our plans into action. I should be sorry if by my negligence our daughter were left unhappily situated, in the care of indifferent guardians. She will be happier in her own home than in ours. We must protect her,

175

too, from the malice of the vulgar tongue, for however chaste she may be she cannot altogether escape censure and slander. And nothing more surely preserves the good reputation of a young girl than an early marriage. I do not think anyone in the city would refuse an alliance with us. Any man would be happy to possess such a jewel as Melibea, one which unites in itself the four things chiefly looked for in a wife; that is to say, firstly, discretion, honesty, and virginity; secondly, beauty; thirdly, noble birth and parentage; and fourthly, wealth! She has been endowed with all these. And if anyone desires more accomplishments, they too are to be found in her.

ALISA. God keep her safe, my lord Pleberio, and grant that our wishes may be fulfilled in our lifetime. But for my part I do not think there is anyone worthy of your daughter! With her virtue and your honoured name there can be few who deserve her. But that is your affair and nothing to do with me! I shall be happy to agree to whatever you think fit, and our daughter, too, will obey you chastely and humbly, in all honesty, as she has been taught to do.

LUCRETIA. Oh, if you but knew the truth how bitterly you would weep! Calisto has had the best of her, and now that Celestina is dead there is no one to restore a lost maidenhead. You come too late! You should have got up earlier! Listen, lady Melibea!

MELIBEA. What are you hiding there for, foolish wench?

LUCRETIA. Come here, lady, and you will hear what a hurry your parents are in to get you married!

MELIBEA. Be quiet, for God's sake, they will hear you! Let them chatter, let them babble on! They have talked of nothing else for the past month! They seem to have no other subject of conversation! Sometimes I wonder if they have guessed my love for Calisto, and know all that has passed between us this last month? I do not know whether they suspect anything. I do not know what is in their minds, but they seem to spend all their time worrying about getting me married. But I am afraid their labour will be in vain! It is too late to shut the stable door when the horse has been stolen! Nothing will make me give up my beloved! No one shall take my happiness from me! Calisto is my soul, my life, my lord, in whom I place all my trust. I know he will never be unfaithful to me. He loves me so much, it is only fair I should love him in return! In this world all debts must be paid in kind. Love will take nothing but love. The thought of him rejoices my heart; the sight of him delights my eye; the sound of his voice pleases my ear. He may ask of me what he will, I will give it gladly. If he decides to cross the seas I will go with him; if he wishes to travel by land he must take me too; if he sells me into slavery in the land of my enemies I will submit to it. My parents must let me have him if they wish to keep me. They need not trouble about such trifling things as marriage, for it is better to be a good mistress than a bad wife. If they look forward to a tranquil old age they must let me enjoy the pleasures of youth. Otherwise they will betray me and dig their own graves! The only thing I regret is the time wasted before I knew and enjoyed Calisto. I do not want a husband. I will not defame the marriage bed, nor allow a husband to tread in the footsteps of my lover, though, if I can believe all I read, many ladies, older, better born, and of higher estate than I, have done so! And some were regarded by the heathen as goddesses! Venus, the mother of Aeneas and of Cupid, the god of love, was married and broke the oath sworn to her husband. Others, devoured by burning passion, committed incestuous and infamous faults, among them Mirra with her father, Semiramis with her son, Canace with her brother, and the unhappy Tamar too, daughter of King David. Others wantonly broke the laws of nature, like Pasiphae, wife of King Minos, with the bull. But they were queens and great ladies, and before their crimes mine, which is natural and of no great account, pales into insignificance! Love came to me naturally, and with good reason. It was sought for, prayed for. I was taken prisoner by Calisto's merits and by Celestina's wiles. Already seduced by her dangerous conversation, I ended by yielding my person to his love. And for the last month, as you know, never a night has passed without our orchard walls being scaled, as if this house were a fortress! Often he has climbed them in vain, yet never once has he shown anger or discontent. For me two of his servants have been put to death. His fortune diminishes, he has given up all his friends in the city; all day he stays shut up at home, living in hope of seeing me at night. Far be it from me to be ungrateful to such a lover, far be it from me to flatter and betray him! Since I have so faithful a lover I have no need of husband, parents, or kinsmen. Lacking Calisto, I should lack life itself, which pleases me only because he takes pleasure in me.

LUCRETIA. Quietly, lady! Listen, they are still talking!

PLEBERIO. Wife, do you think I should speak to our daughter? Should I tell her which men have sought her hand in marriage, so that she can tell us frankly which one of them best pleases her? For although our children must submit to our authority, yet our laws allow them some liberty of choice.

ALISA. What are you thinking of! It would be pure waste of time! Do you not realize that our Melibea would be terrified at the mere mention of such a thing? Do you suppose she knows what a man is? Or even that they marry, and how they marry? Or that from the union of men and women children are born? Go to, do you think her virgin innocence can understand a shameful desire she knows nothing of, and has never even heard of? Do you think she can sin, even in thought? Never believe it, lord Pleberio! You have only to command. Whether the man be of high birth or low, handsome or ugly, she will accept him, she will incline to him, if you say so. I know how I have brought her up!

MELIBEA. Lucretia, Lucretia, run quickly! Go in by the little door and interrupt their conversation! Stop their praises of me on some pretext or other or I shall scream like a madwoman! I cannot bear to hear them praising my innocence!

LUCRETIA. I go, lady!

ACT SEVENTEEN

SUMMARY: *Elicia, who is no Penelope, decides to stop grieving for her three dead friends! She admits that Areusa's advice was sound and goes to her house. Sosia arrives soon after, and Areusa, with judicious flattery, gets from him a full and complete account of Calisto's clandestine meetings with Melibea.*

ELICIA. Oh, how tired I am of my mourning! Hardly anyone comes to see me; the street is deserted; no one wakes me with music or comes to sing before my door, no one riots and fights at night for my sake! And, what is worse, no money or presents pass my threshold! I have only myself to thank for all this! If I had listened to the advice my kind sister Areusa, who loves me well, gave me when I first broke to her the sad news which has plunged me into this penury, I should not now find myself alone in these four walls, with never a friend to cheer me up. Why the devil should I grieve for him? I don't suppose my death would have caused him a pang! She said to me frankly, 'Sister, never grieve for others more than they would grieve for you!' Sempronio would have been glad if I had died! Why should I be so foolish as to weep for him? Who knows, he might even have killed me, he was so mad and crazy, instead of the old woman, whom I looked on as a mother? I shall take Areusa's advice. She knows more about these things than I do. I will go and see her, and learn from her how to get the best out of life. What an agreeable creature she is! How witty and amusing her conversation! Truly they say that an hour in the company of a wise man is worth a lifetime with a fool! I will lay aside my mourning, forget my grief, dry my tears which flow too freely. But it is

not surprising that our tears begin so easily and are so hard to
stop, for the first sound we utter when we come into this world
is a cry! But I must be sensible, for I know that so much
weeping will ruin my looks. I know too that art can make a
woman seem beautiful even if she is not! It makes an old
woman look young, and a young one younger still! Paint
and powder are so much bird-lime, which serves to trap the
young men. Come then, my mirror and my face lotions, let
me repair the damage to my eyes! On with my white coif, my
embroidered ruff, my most beautiful clothes! I must prepare
a wash for my hair, which has lost its golden sheen. That
done, I will count the hens, make my bed—for tidiness makes
a woman's heart rejoice—sweep before my door, and sprinkle
water in the street, so that all who pass by may know that grief
no longer lodges here! But first of all I will go and visit my
cousin and ask her if she has seen Sosia, and what passed
between them. For I have not seen him since I sent him to
her house. Pray God I may find her alone, for she is always
surrounded by a crowd of men, like an inn full of drunkards!
The door is shut—I don't think there is anyone with her. I
will knock! Rat-tat!

AREUSA. Who is there?

ELICIA. Open, dear friend! It is Elicia!

AREUSA. Come in, my dear sister! Now, as God's my witness, I am glad to see you have discarded your mourning!
Now we can enjoy ourselves and visit each other, either at your
house or at mine! Perhaps Celestina's death will prove to be
a blessing in disguise, for already I find I am getting on much
better than I did! That is why they say the dead open the
eyes of the living—some by wealth, some by liberty—as it is
with you too!

ELICIA. Someone is knocking at the door! We haven't had
much chance to talk! I wanted to ask you if Sosia had been
here?

AREUSA. No, he hasn't! But we must talk about it later. What a knocking! It's either a madman or one of my clients! Who is there?

SOSIA. Open the door, lady, it is Sosia, servant of Calisto!

AREUSA. Talk of the devil! Hide behind this screen, sister, and you will hear how I handle him! I will so flatter him that on leaving here he will think he is the only man in the world! I will get out of him all his secrets, and his master's, as easily as he wipes the dust from his horses' hides! Is that you, Sosia, my dear, secret friend? He whom I love though he knows it not? He whom I have long desired to meet, because of his great reputation? They tell me you are so fond of your master, such a good friend to all your companions! I must embrace you, my love! Now I see you I believe you are even more wonderful than I thought! You have a look of my poor Parmeno. Well, it was a lucky day that brought you to my door! Tell me, my dear, did you know me before?

SOSIA. Lady, you have such a reputation in our city for beauty, wit, and wisdom that you must not be surprised if you are known to more men than you know! No one can speak in praise of a fair woman without remembering that you are the fairest of them all!

ELICIA. (Well, the old son of a whore! He brays like an ass! Who would have thought, seeing him take his horses to water, riding barebacked, his legs dangling below his ragged tunic, that he could so strut it in doublet and hose, with nodding plumes, and a false, lying tongue!)

AREUSA. Oh, I should be ashamed if anyone heard you say such things! You are making fun of me! You are just like all the others! You have a stock of gallant phrases, deceitful flatteries, all after the same pattern, which you hand out to all of us! But I am not taken in! And I assure you, Sosia, you need not trouble to flatter me! Before you even begin to

woo I am won! I asked you to come and see me for two
reasons. But if you are going to lie to me I will not tell you
what they are, even though it would be to your advantage!

SOSIA. Lady, God forbid that I should lie to you! I came
here, not knowing the great esteem in which you say you hold
me. I do not feel myself worthy to undo your shoes! You
may direct my speech, frame my replies to your questions, and
I will agree to whatever you say!

AREUSA. My love, you know how fond I was of Parmeno,
and, as the saying goes: 'Love me, love my friend!' So I love
everyone he loved. All his friends are my friends, and faithful
service done to his master pleases me as much as if it were
done to me. When danger menaced Calisto I helped him to
avert it. I tell you all this so that you may understand why I
am so fond of you, and why your visits will always be so
welcome. You will not lose by it if I can help it. There will
always be something for you! The second thing is, I beg you,
now you know how fond I am of you, and how much I desire
your company, to be careful not to run into danger. Keep
your secrets to yourself. For see what happened to Sempronio
and Parmeno, only because they gave away Celestina's secrets!
I do not want you to die as they did. It was bad enough to
have to weep for them! Now you must know that someone
has been to see me, and has told me that you have told him all
about Calisto and Melibea—how he has made her his mistress,
and goes every night to visit her, and how you go with him,
and many other things which I need not repeat. Have a care,
my friend, it is all too true that it is not only women who
cannot keep a secret; and not all of them, of course, but only
the giddy girls and feather-brains! So be careful, for you may
be in great danger. Remember, God gave you two eyes and
two ears, but only one tongue, to remind you to speak only
half of what you see and hear! Be very careful! Why should
you expect your friends to keep your secrets if you cannot

keep them yourself? When you have to follow Calisto to
Melibea's house, go very quietly, do not make the slightest
sound. For I am told that you go rollicking along as if you
were drunk with excitement!

SOSIA. Anyone who has told you that, lady, is a telltale and a
tattler! If he says he heard Calisto's secret from my lips he
lies! They have seen me go out by moonlight to water my
horses. Then I sing and whistle to keep up my spirits, and
help me forget my fatigue—and never later than ten o'clock at
night! They have misjudged me and taken their suspicions
for certainties! Calisto is not such a fool as to go about his
business so early! He waits until everyone is in bed, enjoying
the first sweet sleep! Nor does he go every night, for that is
not a thing one can do so often! I can prove they are lying
if that is any satisfaction to you. For, as they say: 'You can
catch a liar quicker than a lame man!' In one month we have
only been to Melibea's house about eight times!

AREUSA. Now, on my life, my love, tell me in advance when
you are going out at night, and then I can accuse them and
catch them out in their lies! And when it is proved that they
are not speaking the truth you will be out of danger, and I
shall not have to worry over your safety! I look forward to
enjoying your company for a long time yet!

SOSIA. Lady, let us not wait to put it to the proof! For this
very night, when the clock strikes twelve, he will visit her in
the orchard! Ask your friends about it to-morrow and I dare
be sworn they will not have heard a word of it!

AREUSA. Which way will you go, my dear? Then if they tell
me wrong I can convict them of error!

SOSIA. By the street of the fat friar, where it runs behind his
house.

ELICIA. (You are sucked dry, my poor ragged lad, and we have
no further need of you! I am sorry for anyone who entrusts
his secrets to this muleteer, for he will tell all!)

AREUSA. Brother Sosia, it is understood! I have enough evidence to prove your innocence and the wickedness of your enemies! Now go with God, for I am much occupied with another matter and we have wasted too much time already!

ELICIA. (O clever one! What a leave-taking! He deserves it for parting so lightly with his secrets!)

SOSIA. Gracious and charming lady, forgive me if I have wearied you with my chatter! But as long as you are pleased to make use of me, you will never need to seek one more willing to give his life in your service! May the holy angels protect you!

AREUSA. God be with you! Off you go, muleteer! You are proud now, but you'll get no further than looking! Forgive me if I turn my back on you! Well, sister, what did I tell you? Come here and tell me what you thought of the way I sent him off? So I treat all such fools! They leave me as that one did, bruised and beaten! The idiots are confounded; the discreet affrighted; the pious troubled; the chaste enflamed! You see, cousin, my art is quite different from Celestina's! She thought me a fool because I wanted her to think so! And now we know all we need in this matter, so let us go to the house of that creature with the hangdog look whom you saw leaving here last Thursday in such a bad temper! Behave as if you were trying to reconcile us, and make him believe that it was only for your sake that I agreed to visit him at all!

ACT EIGHTEEN

SUMMARY: *Elicia agrees to Areusa's suggestion that she should pretend to reconcile Areusa and Centurio. They go together to his house, where they beg him to avenge the deaths of Sempronio, Parmeno, and Celestina on Calisto and Melibea. He agrees to do so while they are with him, but, as is only to be expected of such a man, he does not keep his promise as will presently appear.*

ELICIA. Is there anyone at home?

CENTURIO. Run, boy! See who dares to enter without knocking. No, come back! I can see who it is. Do not muffle yourself in your cloak, madam, there is no need for you to hide! When I saw Elicia coming I knew she would not be bringing bad news, or an unwelcome guest, but rather someone whose visit would give me pleasure!

AREUSA. Let us not go in! On my life, the wretched creature is already puffed up with pride, thinking I come to plead with him! He would be happier in the company of women of his own kind. Let us turn back, for God's sake, for I am sick of seeing his ugly face! Really, cousin, you put me in a very awkward position! It hardly seems right to come straight from vespers to such a wretch as this!

ELICIA. Come back for my sake! Do not leave us! If you do you will leave half your cloak in my hands.

CENTURIO. Hold fast, lady! By God, hold fast! Don't let her escape you!

ELICIA. I am surprised at you, cousin! What man would be so foolish and so unreasonable as not to enjoy being visited, particularly by a woman? Come nearer, sir Centurio, I am

determined that she shall embrace you, whether she will or no!
And I will take the blame!

AREUSA.   Embrace him!   I would sooner see him in prison
or dying at the hands of his enemies than give him that pleasure!
No, no!   All is over between us for ever!   What has my
enemy ever done for me that I should embrace him or even
look on him?   The other day, when I asked him to do a simple
errand for me, something that touched me very nearly and
entailed only a day's journey, would he do it?   No!

CENTURIO.   Lady, ask me to do something that comes within
my scope and I will do it gladly!   Ask me to challenge three
men, and however many more may turn up I will take them
all on for love of you!   To kill a man, cut off a leg or an arm,
scar the face of any woman who thinks herself your equal in
beauty—such trifling things I will do before you ask!   But
don't ask me to go a long journey on foot or to lend you
money, for you know I never have any!   I could turn upside-
down and not a coin would fall from my pockets!   No man
can give more than he has.   In my house you can walk about
freely without fearing to knock things over!   All my gear is
that of a soldier in the field—a cracked water-jar, a blunted
spit!   The bed on which I sleep is a pile of broken buckler-
straps, with a bit of old chain-mail for mattress and a dice-
box for pillow!   When I want to entertain my friends I have
nothing left to pawn but this ragged old cloak which hangs
about my shoulders!

ELICIA.   I must say I am very touched by what he tells us!
He is as humble as a blessed saint, he speaks to you like an
angel, he agrees with all you say!   What more can you ask?
On my life, speak to him!   Do not be angry with him any
longer!   He has done his best to please you.

CENTURIO.   To please her, you say, lady?   I swear by all the
catalogue of saints and martyrs from A to Z that my arm
quivers already at the thought of what I am going to do for

her! I am always trying to please her, and never succeed.
Last night I dreamed that for her sake I challenged and fought
with four men, whom she knows well, and that I killed one of
them. The others fled, and the luckiest left a severed arm at
my feet. So judge how much more I shall do by day, when I
am awake, and find someone who has offended her!

AREUSA. Since we are here this is a good opportunity to take
you at your word! I forgive you, on condition that you
avenge me on a knight named Calisto, who has offended both
me and my cousin here!

CENTURIO. Oh, no conditions! Just give him time to make
his peace with heaven!

AREUSA. You need not bother about the state of his soul!

CENTURIO. Very well! We'll send him to dine in hell
without shriving!

AREUSA. Now listen, and don't interrupt me! You must kill
him to-night!

CENTURIO. Not another word! I have all I want! I know
all about him and his love, those who have died because of it,
and how you are concerned in the matter. I know where he
is going, to whom, and at what time. Tell me only this!
How many men will there be with him?

AREUSA. Two!

CENTURIO. That's not very many! My sword will find little
work to do there. It would be better employed in another
little party to which I am bidden to-night!

AREUSA. You say that to put me off! Let the other dogs
gnaw their own bones! All this shilly-shallying means
nothing to me! All I want to know is, will you do as I ask
or not?

CENTURIO. If my sword had to say what it was going to do
there would not be time enough left to do it! What else fills
the cemeteries? What else has so enriched the surgeons of
this city? What else cuts through the finest chain-mail,

pierces the shields of Barcelona, cleaves through the helmets
of Calatayud, and carves up the casques of Almazán like ripe
melons? It has kept me in food and drink these twenty years,
and made me feared by men and sought after by women!
Because of it my grandfather was called Centurio, so was my
father, and so am I.

ELICIA. But how did a sword help your grandfather to such a
name? Did it make him master of a hundred men?

CENTURIO. No, but it helped him to keep a hundred women!

AREUSA. What have we to do with your ancestors and their
exploits? If you are willing to do what I ask say so without
more ado, for we must be going!

CENTURIO. I am more anxious for night to fall so that I may
do your bidding than you to know it done! And so as not to
leave anything to chance you yourself shall choose the manner
of his death. I can show you, here and now, my repertory of
seven hundred and seventy different kinds of death. You can
choose the one you like best.

ELICIA. Areusa, for God's sake do not entrust this affair to
such a cruel man! It would be better to wait than to scan-
dalize the whole city. That would do us more harm than
anything that has happened yet!

AREUSA. Hold your tongue, sister! Tell me of a death which
comes without a sound.

CENTURIO. The methods I have used recently, which therefore come most easily to me at the moment, are blows on the
back with a sheathed sword—this draws no blood!—or with
the pommel of the sword. Then there is the quick stab in the
back. Some I stick full of little holes, others I carve up with
deep gashes, fearful to behold, mortal wounds! Some I club
to death to give my sword a rest!

ELICIA. No more for God's sake! Beat him well to punish
him, but do not kill him!

CENTURIO. I swear by all the saints in the litany that it is as impossible for me to beat a man without killing him as it is for the sun to stand still in the heavens!

AREUSA. Sister, we must be merciless! Let him do it any way he pleases, and kill as it suits him best! Let Melibea weep as you have wept! Leave it all to him! Centurio, be sure to do as I ask! However he dies I shall be content. But see that he does not escape the just punishment of his crime!

CENTURIO. May God forgive him if he escapes me any way but by flight! I am glad, my dear, that an occasion has arisen, however slight, to show you what I will do for love of you!

AREUSA. May God guide your right hand! I commend you to Him! Now we must go!

CENTURIO. God be with you too and give you more patience with your friends! To the devil with these impudent whores! Now I must find a way of getting out of keeping my promise! But it must be done in such a manner that they will think I have diligently performed their bidding. I should be in great danger if they suspected me of negligence! I could pretend to be ill. But what's the use? They would only wait until I was well again! If I say I attacked them and put them all to flight they will want proof of it. They will ask me how many there were, where I met them, what they were wearing! And I shall not know what to say. I am in a tight corner! How can I satisfy their demands at no risk to myself? I will go and see Traso, the lame boy, and his two friends, and tell them that as I am to be busy to-night about another matter they must go and create a disturbance, with swords and bucklers, as if fighting in the street, to frighten some young men I will tell them of. I will say I was asked to do it, but cannot. That it is just a joke and there is no danger. They need only frighten the men away, and then they can return home and go back to bed!

ACT NINETEEN

SUMMARY: *Calisto, Sosia, and Tristan go to Pleberio's orchard, where Melibea is waiting with Lucretia. On the way there Sosia tells Tristan of his interview with Areusa. While Calisto is in the orchard with Melibea Traso and his friends arrive, sent by Centurio to carry out the promise he made to Areusa and Elicia. Sosia goes to meet them. Calisto hears the noise in the street and goes to see what is happening. This leads to his death—the usual reward of such lovers, which should teach them that it is better not to love at all than to love in such a sort.*

SOSIA. Go quietly and then no one will hear us! On the way to Pleberio's orchard I will tell you, friend Tristan, what passed to-day between me and Areusa, which makes me the happiest man in the world! You must know that she has heard such a good report of me that she has fallen in love with me! She sent Elicia to ask me to go and see her, and after giving me a lot of good advice, which I won't trouble you with she told me plainly that she is now as much mine as she was Parmeno's. She begged me to visit her as often as I liked, and said she hoped to enjoy my company for a long time to come. I swear to you, brother, on my life, by the dangerous road we tread, that I was several times tempted to take her at her word! But I was rather taken aback and shamed to see her so beautiful and well dressed, while I was wearing only this moth-eaten old cloak! Every time she moved she smelt of musk, while I smelt of the horse-dung that clung to my boots. Her hands were white as snow, and as she took off her gloves they perfumed the room with the scent of orange-water. Besides, she was busy; so I reserved my ardour for another day! One cannot do everything at a first visit! The more one talks the sooner one comes to an understanding!

TRISTAN. Friend Sosia, it would need someone more experienced than I to advise you in this matter. But though I am young and untried I can at least give you my opinion. This woman is a well-known whore by what you have told me. You must make sure that there is no deception on her side. Her offers may be false, though I do not quite see what she hopes to gain by them. If she says she loves you because you are handsome she has had many more handsome; if because you are rich she knows you have nothing but the dust which flies from your curry-comb; if because you are a gentleman she knows you are called Sosia, and so was your father, and that you were born and brought up in a village, where you proved yourself a better ploughman than lover! Take care, Sosia! Find out first if she is not trying to get out of you the secret of this enterprise we are now engaged on, so that she can make Calisto and Pleberio suffer for the happiness of Melibea, which makes her so jealous! Take care, for jealousy, once contracted, is an incurable malady, a troublesome guest which fatigues his host and enjoys nothing more than the unhappiness of others! If things stand thus this wicked woman has beguiled you with the notorious tricks for which she is famous! She seeks to appease her sufferings by poisoning your mind and damning your soul to hell! She will stop at nothing to accomplish her wicked design! O most pernicious woman! For bread she will give you a stone; she will sell her body to further the damnable cause she has at heart! Hear me, and if you think I am right be prepared to deal double with her; for they say: 'Set a thief to catch a thief!' You get my meaning? He who sups with the devil . . .! Thwart her malicious schemes, see that her wicked plans go awry, and when you have turned matters to your own profit you can sit snugly in your stable and say: 'You can lead a horse to the water, but you cannot make him drink!'

SOSIA. Tristan, you are a sensible lad, much wiser than your

years! You have raised a suspicion in my mind which is, I
think, justified! But here we are at the orchard and our
master approaches. We must break off our conversation.
There is much to discuss, but it must wait for a better
time!

CALISTO. Lads, put up the ladder! And now be silent, for I
think I hear my lady singing! I will go quietly to the top of
the wall, and there I will listen to hear if she sighs for me in
my absence!

MELIBEA. Sing again, Lucretia, I beg you, for it pleases me to
hear you! Sing until my love comes! Sing softly among
these leafy trees, so that passers-by cannot hear!

LUCRETIA.   I would I had the power
                  To revive these lovely flowers
                  That die upon the hour
                  That you depart these bowers!
                  The lily and the rose
                  With fresher hues would burn,
                  And petals all unclose
                  To herald your return!

MELIBEA. Oh, how this song delights me! I am lost in
wonder! Do not stop! Sing again, for love of me!

LUCRETIA.   Oh, welcome is the rill
                  To drink at, being dry,
                  But you more welcome still
                  To your Melibea's eye!
                  Come when night is nigh
                  And use me as you will!
                  The orchard walls are high,
                  But come, for good or ill!
                  The lambkins all rejoice
                  To hear the ewe, iwis,
                  And when I hear your voice
                  I long to feel your kiss!

> Never a place so blest
> As this, so set apart,
> Where first Calisto pressed
> Melibea to his heart!

MELIBEA. Dear Lucretia, I feel and see everything as you
describe it! It is as if Calisto were here before my very eyes!
Sing again, for you sing well, and I will join in.

LUCRETIA and
MELIBEA.   Trees from your leafy height
                  Bend your heads low before
                  The heavenly presence bright
                  Of him whom I adore!
                  Stars in the heavens above
                  Shine out, no longer hide!
                  Awake my sleeping love,
                  And bring him to my side!

MELIBEA. Now I will sing alone! Listen!
                  Nightingales that all night
                  Sing until it be day,
                  Go ask my faithless knight
                  Why he thus stays away?
                  Now in the skies above
                  Heralds of dawn I see!
                  Say, does a newer love
                  Keep him from me?

CALISTO. Oh, I am overcome by the sweetness of your song!
I can no longer bear to keep you in suspense! O my lady and
my life, was ever woman born who could compare with you?
O sweet melody! O joyful moment! O my heart, could you
not bear to wait a moment longer before interrupting her sweet
song and accomplishing our mutual desire?

MELIBEA. O sweet treason! O happy surprise! Is that my
lord and my soul? It is he! I cannot believe it! Where
were you, my shining sun? Where had you hidden your

brilliance? Have you been listening long? Why did you let
me mar the silence of the night with these poor verses, sung in
my hoarse swan's croak? All the orchard rejoices when you
are here! See, the moon throws her sweet light so that we
may see each other, the clouds fly away, the cool waters of the
fountain rise up from the fresh green grass with a soft murmuring sound! Listen to the tall cypresses! How sweetly their
branches kiss in the gentle breeze! See their quiet shadows!
How ready they are to hide us safely in our joy! Lucretia,
what are you thinking of? Have you gone mad with joy?
Leave him alone, do not drag him from me, do not tire him
with your embraces! Let me enjoy him, for he is mine! Do
not seek to steal away my pleasure!

CALISTO. My lady and my love, if you wish to make me happy
continue your sweet singing! Do not let my presence, in
which you take pleasure, be less agreeable than my absence,
which so grieves you!

MELIBEA. What shall I sing, my lord? How can I sing now?
It was my longing for you which set free my voice and made
me sing! Now you are here my every wish is fulfilled and my
song is hushed! But, sir, since you are the model of courtesy
and good manners, how can you command me to sing and
not command the straying of your importunate hands! Bid
them desist from their wicked ways! Tell them to be still,
to stop their wanderings and their insupportable temerity!
Softly, my angel, for much as I love to see you sitting quietly
beside me, I am distressed when you treat me so roughly. A
little sporting delights me, but your hands are too bold, they
weary me beyond measure. Do not disarrange my dress! If
you want to know whether my shift is of silk or linen, there is
no need to tumble me! I tell you frankly, it is linen! Let us
sport and play in a hundred ways which I can show you, but
do not tousle me and disrobe me as you usually do! What is
the good of tearing my garments?

CALISTO.   Lady, he who wishes to enjoy the bird must first pluck it!

LUCRETIA.   Pox take me if I can bear to listen to them any longer!   What a to-do!   It sets my teeth on edge!   She resists him to make him more eager!   Good, good, the argument is over!   They didn't need a peacemaker!   I could do as much if these fools of servants would only come and visit me by night!   But they wait for me to go to them!

MELIBEA.   My lord, can I send Lucretia to fetch you anything?

CALISTO.   I want nothing but your white body and the certainty that your beauty is for me alone!   Money will buy food and drink in any market!   They can be had at short notice and enjoyed by everyone!   But here, in this orchard, is merchandise which is not to be bought, and has no equal in all the world.   How can you expect me to forgo for one single instant the enjoyment of it?

LUCRETIA.   Oh, my head aches to hear them!   They never tire of talking, nor their arms of embracing, nor their lips of kissing!   Ah, they are quiet now!   Let us hope it will last this time!

CALISTO.   O my beloved, I wish day would never break!   Then I could enjoy eternally the bliss I now feel in the contemplation and delight of your delicate limbs!

MELIBEA.   My lord, I am happy in your love, for you honour me with your attentions, and I am the gainer by them!

SOSIA.   Now then, you rogues, you rascals, do you dare to attack us?   We are not afraid of you!   I swear, if you so much as touch me, you will get what you deserve!

CALISTO.   Lady, that is Sosia's voice!   I must go and make sure that he is in no danger.   There is only a young page with him.   Give me my cloak—you are lying on it!

MELIBEA.   Oh, unlooked-for interruption!   Do not go without your cuirass.   Come back, arm yourself!

CALISTO.　Lady, that which a sword, a cloak, and a bold heart cannot do will never be done by a cuirass, a helmet, and cowardice!

SOSIA.　Are you still there?　Wait till I come!　You came to shear, and may return home shorn!

CALISTO.　For God's sake let me go, my love!　The ladder is there, waiting for me!

MELIBEA.　O unhappy Melibea!　Why do you rush off so rashly, impatient and unarmed, without knowing what danger may lie in wait for you?　Lucretia, come here quickly! Calisto has gone!　He heard a noise in the street.　Throw his breast-plate over the wall—he has left it behind!

TRISTAN.　Stay, sir, do not come down—they have fled!　There was only the lame Traso, with some other rogues, who passed shouting and rioting along the street.　Sosia is just coming back.　Hold on to the ladder, sir!　Grip it with both your hands!

CALISTO.　Oh, the Holy Virgin protect me!　I am dead!　I am dead!

TRISTAN.　Sosia, come here, come quickly!　Our poor master has fallen off the ladder!　He won't move or speak to me!

SOSIA.　Sir, sir!　He doesn't hear me—he's as dead as a door-nail!　Oh, what a terrible thing to happen!

LUCRETIA.　Listen, listen!　Something terrible has happened!

MELIBEA.　What is it?　What do I hear?　O unhappy that I am!

TRISTAN.　My lord is dead!　My master has killed himself! He died before he had time to confess his sins!　Sosia, help me to gather up his brains from among these stones; try to put them back in his cracked skull!　O bitter blow!　O unexpected end!

MELIBEA.　O wretched girl!　What has happened?　What terrible thing is he talking about?　Help me to climb up the

O 100

ladder, Lucretia, so that I can see if what I suspect is true, or I will raise the roof of my father's house with my cries and lamentations! Alas, my joy is fled, my glory dissipated in smoke! Lost is my quiet! I am consumed by despair!

LUCRETIA. Tristan, boy, tell me, why are you crying so bitterly?

TRISTAN. I weep for my loss and the great grief I feel! My master Calisto has fallen off the ladder and he is dead! His head is broken in pieces! Alas, he died unshriven! Tell his sorrowing lady not to wait any longer for her unfortunate lover! Sosia, take up his feet; let us carry away the body of our beloved master, so that his honour may not suffer through his death in such a place! Let us go alone, in tears, desolate and disconsolate! Let us put on sackcloth and ashes and sit weeping for our master!

MELIBEA. O most wretched Melibea! So short a time I have known happiness, and now, almost at once, grief follows after!

LUCRETIA. Madam, do not tear your hair, do not beat your breast! A moment of pleasure, and now pain! What planet has suddenly changed its course? Do not be so faint-hearted, madam! Get up, for God's sake, and do not let your father find you here! Heaven knows what he will suspect! Lady, lady, do you not hear me? For the love of heaven do not swoon away! Show as much courage in your loss as you did in committing your fault!

MELIBEA. Did you hear what his servants said? They are taking away my joy, and he is dead! Do you hear their sad murmurs? They are lifting up my whole world from the cold ground! All hope is fled! I can no longer bear to live! Why did I not enjoy my felicity longer? Why did I think so little of the jewel I held in my hands? Oh, how ungrateful is man! He never appreciates his good fortune until it is taken from him!

LUCRETIA. Take heart, look up, madam! You will bring
more grief and shame on yourself if you are found in the
orchard, more than enough to outweigh the pleasure you had
in his company and your grief at his loss! Come back to
your room—go to bed!   And since your tears cannot be hidden
we must pretend they spring from some other cause!

ACT TWENTY

SUMMARY: *Lucretia knocks at the door of Pleberio's room. He asks her what she wants. Lucretia begs him to go and see his daughter, so he gets up and goes to Melibea's room. He consoles her, and she asks him to fetch her some musical instruments. Meanwhile she and Lucretia climb up the tower. Melibea sends Lucretia down again and locks the door. When her father comes to the foot of the tower she tells him all that has happened, and then throws herself down.*

PLEBERIO. What is it, Lucretia? Why are you in such a hurry? What do you want with your impetuosity and hysterics? Has something happened to my daughter? It must have been very sudden. You don't give me time to get dressed, hardly even to get up!

LUCRETIA. Sir, hurry if you wish to see your daughter alive, for I do not know what is the matter with her! She has suddenly been taken ill! She is so altered that I hardly recognize her!

PLEBERIO. Come quickly then! We will go in together. Go in first! Pull aside the curtains and open the shutters so that I can see her clearly. What is the matter, my daughter? Are you in pain? What has happened? What, not a word? Look up, it is your father! Speak to me! For God's sake tell me what is the matter, so that something can be done at once to relieve your sufferings! You are killing me with anxiety! You know I have no other child but you! Open your eyes, look at me!

MELIBEA. Oh, I suffer!

PLEBERIO. I suffer as much as you to see you so ill! Your mother is prostrate with grief at the news of your sudden illness. She could not come and see you, she was so distressed. Take courage, lift up your head, try to sit up! Come with me

200

to your mother!   Tell me, my darling, what has caused your
suffering?

MELIBEA.   It is past cure!   The remedy is lost!

PLEBERIO.   My beloved daughter, treasure of your father's old
age, for God's sake do not let yourself despair!   Do not
torment yourself and think your illness and suffering past
cure!   Pain only afflicts the feeble-hearted!   If only you will
tell me what ails you, remedies will soon be found.   We do
not lack medicines, doctors, and servants to help you back to
health, whether it lies hidden in stones or charms or in the
secret parts of animals!   Do not keep me any longer in
suspense!   Do not torment me, do not drive me to despair, but
tell me plainly, what is the matter?

MELIBEA.   I have a deep wound in my heart which will not let
me rest.   It is no ordinary malady I suffer from.   To cure it
you must tear out my heart, for it lies hidden in the innermost
part of me!

PLEBERIO.   You are young to feel such pain, reserved usually
for old age!   Young people should be happy and carefree,
and know nothing of sorrow and despair.   Get up, my dear!
Come and breathe the fresh air on the river bank!   It will do
you good, and you will soon feel better when you are with
your mother.   Make an effort!   Nothing will do you more
good than that.   It is a sovereign remedy.

MELIBEA.   I will do as you suggest.   But, dear father, let us
mount to the top of the high tower!   From there I can watch
the ships go by.   Perhaps that will make me feel better.

PLEBERIO.   Certainly, let us go up!   Lucretia, come with us!

MELIBEA.   If it please you, dear father, send for some stringed
instruments so that I may distract my thoughts with singing
and playing; and if my sufferings get worse I can soothe them
with sweet sounds and soft harmonies.

PLEBERIO.   It shall be done at once, my daughter!   I will go
and fetch them myself.

MELIBEA.   Lucretia, my friend, we are very high up here!   I
am sorry I sent my father away.   Run after him and ask him
to come to the foot of the tower, for I forgot to send a message
to my mother.

LUCRETIA.   I go, lady!

MELIBEA.   Now I am alone!   Everything falls out well for the
death I have decided on.   I feel better already to think that
we shall so soon be together again, I and my lover, my loved
one, Calisto!   First I must lock the door, so that no one can
come in and stop me from leaving this world.   Nothing must
prevent my death.   No one must be allowed to hinder me on
my way to visit my lover, who came to see me last night.   All
has fallen out as I hoped.   Soon I shall be able to tell my
father Pleberio the reason for my fatal resolution.   I shall
bring sorrow to his white hairs, great unhappiness to his last
years.   Many troubles will light upon him because of my sin.
It may be that my death will shorten my parents' lives.   And
yet how many before me have been even more cruel to their
parents!   Prusias, king of Bithynia, for no reason—not
driven to it, as I am, by unhappiness—killed his own father;
Ptolemy, king of Egypt, killed his father, his mother, his
brothers and his wife, so that he might enjoy his concubine.
Orestes killed his mother Clytemnestra, the cruel emperor
Nero his mother Agrippina, simply for the delight he took in
murder.   They truly are murderers and I am not!   If my
death is a cause of sorrow, at least I shall have expiated the
crime I committed.   There were others far more cruel who
killed their sons and brothers.   Beside their crimes mine fades
into insignificance.   Philip, king of Macedonia, Herod, king
of Judaea, Constantine, emperor of Rome, Laodicia, queen
of Cappadocia, Medea, the enchantress—all these killed their
beloved children for no reason and without danger to themselves.   Finally I remember the great cruelty of Phraates,
king of the Parthians, who killed his old father Orodos, and

his only son, and his thirty brothers, so that there should be no
other heir to the throne. They were all guilty of flagrant
crimes, worthy to be punished. Secure from danger themselves, they killed only old men and young children. True it
is that I ought not to imitate them! But everything is now
out of my hands. God, who hears my complaint, take pity on
my weakness! See how my will is taken prisoner! My mind
is so overwhelmed by the weight of my love for Calisto, who is
dead, that I am insensible to the grief of my poor parents, who
are still alive!

PLEBERIO. Daughter Melibea, what are you doing alone up
there? What is it you want to say to me? Shall I come up?

MELIBEA. Dear father, stay where you are! Do not come up
here, for if you do you will make it more difficult for me to
say what must be said. Soon you will weep for the death of
your only child! My end is near! Before long I shall lie in
peace, and you will live in torment! Soon I shall be with my
love, and you alone for ever! Dear father, the time is coming
when you will need not musical instruments to soothe my
sufferings, but passing bells to toll my body to the grave! If
you can listen to me without weeping I will tell you the
desperate cause of my sudden and most happy end. Do not
interrupt me with your groans and lamentations, or you may
suffer more through not knowing the cause of my death than
you will at seeing me dead. Ask me nothing, do not question
me, nor seek to know more than I will tell you! For when the
heart is heavy with grief the ears are closed to good advice.
And at such times the most kindly words wound and do not
calm us. Hear my last words, dear father, and if you receive
them as I hope you will not blame me for my fault! No doubt
you have seen and heard the many signs of mourning which
mount from the whole city? The tolling of bells, the crowds
of people, the barking of dogs, the clash of weapons? I am
the unhappy cause of all this! It is I who have to-day driven

into mourning all the noble families of our town; I have deprived many servants of a good master; I have cut off the supply of alms from many poor unhappy old people! For my sake the dead to-day welcome among them the most accomplished gentleman who ever walked this earth! I have deprived the living of the pattern of all gentleness, of all gallantry, of all graciousness in speech, in gesture, in courtesy, in all virtues! It is because of me that the earth to-day receives for ever the noblest knight and the fairest youth that our age was blessed with! I will tell you plainly what has happened, though I know you will be grieved beyond measure when you hear of my great sin. Many days have passed, dear father, since there fell in love with me a young nobleman named Calisto. You knew him well, you knew his kinsfolk and his noble family! His virtues and his bounty were admired by all! So great was his grief in this love, and so little chance had he of revealing it to me, that he confided his passion to a clever and unscrupulous old woman called Celestina. She came to me with a message from him, and dragged my secret from my bosom. I told her what I had concealed from my own mother! She found a way to overcome my resistance, and so arranged matters that his desires, and mine, were mutually fulfilled. He loved me dearly, and I repaid his love in full. Together we planned how we might carry on this affair. Overcome by love for him, I smuggled him into your house. With the help of a ladder he scaled the orchard walls. He vanquished my chaste resistance and I ceded to him my maidenhead. This delicious fault of love we enjoyed for almost a month. Last night I met him at midnight in the orchard as usual. But fickle fortune, faithless as ever, decided to befriend us no longer! The orchard walls are high, the night was dark, the ladder unsteady, the servants with him not skilled in such matters. He left me suddenly because his servants were fighting in the street. He went so hurriedly that he missed a rung of the ladder and stepped out into space. He fell, and in his disastrous fall his brains were knocked out and strewn all over the walls and the stones of the street. The Fates have cut the thread of his days—they bore him off unshriven! They have cut short my hope, my joy, my delight in his company! How cruel it would be, dear father, to make me live on when he has died so suddenly! His death demands mine! He calls me and I must go at once! He tells me I too must die suddenly, so as to be like him in all things. They shall not say of me: 'Out of sight, out of mind!' I must please him with my death, since I can no longer do so with my life. O Calisto, my love and my lord, wait for me! I am coming! Stay but a moment and I will die with you! Do not blame me for this brief delay! I owe it to my poor old father to give him a final account of myself. Do not grudge him that! It is a debt that must be paid. O my beloved father, I beg you, if you have loved me in this short and sorrowful life, let us have one funeral and be buried in one grave! I wish I had some words of consolation to give you before my most welcome death—some soothing phrases taken from those ancient books you made me read to furnish my mind with wisdom! But my poor brain, caught up in the tumult of my grief, can no longer remember them, especially when I see the tears which you can no longer restrain pour down your wrinkled face! Carry my last farewell to my beloved and loving mother! Tell her freely the sad cause of my death! I am glad she is not here! Take, dear father, this last sad tribute to your respected age! A long life must endure much suffering! Accept the dowry of your old age, and receive in your arms your beloved daughter! I weep for myself, I weep for you, and most of all I weep for my aged mother! God be with you, and with her! To Him I give my soul, and to you this body which now falls beside you!

ACT TWENTY-ONE

SUMMARY: *Pleberio, weeping bitterly, returns to his room, where his wife Alisa asks him the reason for his tears. He tells her of the death of their daughter, and shows her Melibea's body dashed to pieces, ending with great lamentation.*

ALISA. Lord Pleberio, what is the matter? Why are you making such an outcry? I have been lying here, sleepless and almost distracted with worry over our daughter's sudden illness. But I am almost ready to forget my previous preoccupation, so much your groans, your loud cries, your unwonted lamentations, which give proof of despair and desolation, cut me to the heart, pierce through my entrails, and trouble my mind! So one woe drives out another, one grief replaces a former chagrin! Tell me the reason for your tears. Why do you curse your venerable old age and pray for death? Why do you tear out your white hairs and beat your breast? Has something happened to Melibea? For God's sake tell me, for if she suffers I no longer wish to live!

PLEBERIO. Alas, noble wife! Our joy is drowned in sorrow, all our treasure is lost! We have nothing left to live for! Now let death strike you down instantly before you have time to grieve! Come down with me into the grave, so that I may not be alone in my sorrow for the heavy loss which touches us both! Lo, here lies the fruit of your womb, sole issue of my loins, dashed in pieces! She told me the cause of her death before she died, and I have since learned more from her tearful maid. Join me in weeping for our sorrowful old age! O all you who come running at my cries, O my friends and my

206

kinsfolk, help me to support my grief! O my daughter, my dearest treasure! Life without you would be unbearable! My sixty years were riper for the tomb than your twenty! Overcome by sorrow, you have reversed the natural order of things! Surely death would sooner rejoice to carry off my white hairs than your golden tresses, which I see spread out before my eyes? Now shall I know sad days! Have I not reason to complain of death and to accuse him of tardiness? How long must I remain here without you? I lack all things, lacking your pleasant company! O my wife, rise up from our daughter's body, and if you still breathe join with me in sad groans and sighs, in sobbing and lamentation! But if your soul has fled to rejoin hers, if you are already dead of grief, why have you gone without waiting for me? How much happier are women in this than we men, for a great shock will in an instant strike them dead, or at least deprive them of their senses, which is in itself a sort of consolation! O hard heart of a father! Why do you not break at once, since you have been bereft of your only child? For her, and for no one else, I raised these walls, acquired honours, planted trees, built ships! O pitiless earth! Why do you still support my feeble steps? What shelter shall I find in my inconsolable old age? O fickle fortune, minister and steward of our worldly wealth, why did you not confine your cruel and capricious dealings to things that concern me alone? Why did you not take from me my inheritance? Why did you not overthrow my house or strip me of my many possessions? You might then have left me this jewel over which you had no power! Would that the wheel of fortune had brought me sorrow in my youth and a joyous old age, and not reversed the order of things! It is easier to bear misfortune when one is young and strong than when one is old and feeble. O life full of anguish, heavy with misery! O world, world! Many have railed against you and spoken ill of you from hearsay! But I can condemn you from my own experience, for I am one whose hopes have been wrecked by your variable winds, and perished on your treacherous reefs! Hitherto I have kept silent, and not complained of your double-dealing, fearing to excite your anger against this flower which to-day has fallen before your onslaught. But now I am without fear, for I have nothing left to lose. To-day I abhor your treachery. I am like the poor man who tramps the roads, singing at the top of his voice, for he has no fear of footpads. In my youth I believed the world went according to plan. Now my eyes are opened! I have known good and evil fortune, and I know the world is a labyrinth of errors, a fearful wilderness, an abode of wild beasts, a game of chance, a muddy marsh, a thicket of thorns, a high mountain, a stony plain, a prairie full of serpents, a flowering orchard that bears no fruit, a fountain of anxiety, a poisoned sweetness, empty hopes, false happiness, true despair! You lure us, false world, with the glittering bait of your deceitful toys, but in the sweetest morsel we find the sharpest hook! We cannot escape; it holds us fast, prisoner against our will! You promise much, but give us nothing! When we seek the fulfilment of your vain promises, you send us away empty-handed. We embark confidently on the vicious pleasures of your fairgrounds, and when it is too late for us to escape you spring the trap! Many have left you, for fear lest you should leave them. They will know how wise they were when they see how you reward the long and loyal service of this poor old man! You put out our eyes, and then anoint our heads with oil! You oppress us all equally, and no one can complain that he is alone in his adversity! But what alleviation is it to such misery as mine to know that I have companions in misfortune? And yet, unhappy father, how alone I am! Though I torment my poor brain with sad stories of past and present misery, yet I can find no one whose affliction compares with mine! Can I be consoled by the courage and

patience of Paulus Emilius, who bore the loss of two sons in
one week with such fortitude that the Roman people could not
condole with him, but drew strength and consolation from him
in their need? His loss was not like mine, for he was able to
console himself with two adopted sons. How can Pericles,
the Athenian captain, help me to bear my sorrow, or the brave
Xenophon? They lost sons who had been long absent from
their homes. It could not have cost the former much to
master himself and remain serene, or the latter to assure the
messenger who had brought the sad tidings of his son's death
that he would not be punished for it, since he, the father,
did not grieve! Their sorrow is very different from mine.
Or would you rather, ignoble fortune, that I compared myself
to Anaxagoras, and said with him of my beloved daughter's
death: 'Since I am moral, I know that he whom I fathered
must die!' But his son perished in a just cause, while my
Melibea killed herself of her own free will, overcome by the
anguish and torment of love. O heavy loss! O miserable
old man! The more I seek for consolation the less I find to
console me! Even David, king and prophet, who wept over
his son when he was sick unto death, would not weep after he
had died, saying it was foolishness to grieve for what was past
remedy! But he had other children to comfort him in his loss.
And I grieve not so much for her death as for the disastrous
cause of it. Yet losing you, unhappy child, I lose those
thousand fears and troubles which each day harassed me!
Your death alone could free me of anxiety! What shall I do
when I go to your room and find it empty? What shall I do
when I call and you do not answer? Who can fill the great
gap you leave in my life? No one ever lost what I have lost
to-day, not even the brave and noble duke of Genoa, Lambas
de Auria, who, seeing his son mortally wounded, took him up
in his arms and threw him overboard. By such deeds,
though they end in death, men show themselves courageous

and worthy of renown.   But my daughter was driven to her
death by the strong compulsion of love.   Now, deceitful world,
what remedy can you offer my grieving heart?   How can you
expect me to remain here, knowing the vanity of worldly
hopes, the traps, the nets, the baited hooks with which you
take us prisoner?   What have you done with my daughter?
Who will keep me company in my empty house?   Who will
bring happiness to my last declining years?   O love, love, I
did not think you had such strength and power as to kill your
own subjects!   I was your victim in early youth, I too passed
through your fiery furnace!   Now, in my old age, must I pay
the penalty for my escape?   When I reached the age of forty
I thought I was beyond your reach.   I lived peacefully with
my wife, and watched the ripening of the fruit that you have
plucked to-day.   I did not think you would visit the sins of the
fathers upon the children.   I know not whether you strike
with the sword or burn up with fire!   You break our hearts
and leave our garments untouched!   You constrain us to
worship what is ugly, and to find it beautiful!   Who gave you
such power?   Who called you by so unfitting a name as love?
If you were truly love you would love those that follow you.
If you loved them you would not cause them to suffer so.   If
they were happy they would not kill themselves for your sake,
as my dear daughter has done to-day.   What has become of
all your servants and ministers?   The false whore Celestina
died at the hands of her servants—the very ones who had been
most zealous in the prosecution of her wicked designs!   They
died decapitated.   Calisto fell to his death.   My daughter,
desperate to rejoin him, died by the same means.   You, love,
are the cause of all this!   Your name is pleasant, but your
deeds bitter; your rewards unequal, your laws iniquitous, for
you take no account of merit.   Your speech is honeyed, your
conduct infamous.   Happy are those who never know you,
and in whom you take no interest!   Some, driven to madness

by I know not what enchantment, call you a god. A god would not kill his own creation! Yet you have caused the death of many of those who served you. Enemy of good sense, you are prodigal of attentions to those who regard you least, until at last they fall into your power. Enemy of friends, friend of enemies, why is your kingdom so unruly and disordered? They paint you as a poor blind boy, holding in your hand a bow, which you draw at a hazard. But those who minister to you are more blind than you! They never suspect what a cruel reward they will receive for their services! Your onslaught is like lightning, which strikes without warning. The fuel which feeds your flame is compounded of men's souls and bodies. Your victims are so numerous that the memory of man cannot recall the first of them. Not only Christians, but Jews and Gentiles have suffered in payment of their loyal service to you! What can you say of Macías, who in our own day died for love, and of whose sad end you were the sole cause? What happened to Paris, to Helen, to Hypermnestra, to Aegisthus? All the world knows! What of Sappho, or Ariadne, or Leander? What reward did you give them? You did not spare even David and Solomon! Samson paid the penalty of having served you, and was betrayed by the woman to whom you made him pledge his faith. Many others I pass over in silence, for I have a heavy enough complaint of my own to make against you. I seek quarrel with the world because it made me. If I had not existed Melibea would not have been born. If she had not been born she would not have loved. If she had not loved I should not be thus afflicted and disconsolate in my declining years. O my sweet child, my unhappy daughter! Why did you not seek counsel of me before you died? Why did you not take pity on your sorrowing and beloved mother? Why were you so cruel to your poor old father? Why have you left me to despair, weeping and lonely in this vale of tears?